Fourth edition

Project

Workbook
with audio CD
and online practice

2

OXFORD

Tom Hutchinson
Rod Fricker

Introduction

Introductions

My family

1 ✴ Read the text and write the names of the people.

1 _Ryan_
2 _____
3 _____
4 _____
5 _____
6 _____

Hi. My name's Ryan and this is my family. I'm with my brother, my sister, my parents and our dog in our garden. My brother's name is Tom. He's twelve. My sister is seven. Her name's Cathy. My mum's name is Lucy and my dad's name is Stephen. Our dog's name is Spot.

2 ✴ Look at exercise 1. Answer the questions.

1 Who is Tom?
   He is Ryan's _____brother_____.
2 Who is Cathy?
   She is Ryan's _____.
3 Who are Lucy and Stephen?
   They are Ryan's _____.
4 Who is Stephen?
   He is Ryan's _____.
5 Who is Lucy?
   She is Ryan's _____.
6 Who is Spot?
   He is Ryan's _____.

Possessive adjectives

3 ✴✴ Complete the sentences about Ryan and his family. Use *my*, *his*, *her*, *our* or *their*.

'Hi. ¹___*My*___ name's Ryan.'

'This is ²_____ brother. ³_____ name is Tom.'

'This is ⁴_____ sister. ⁵_____ name is Cathy.'

'Hi. ⁶_____ names are Cathy, Ryan and Tom.'

'These are ⁷_____ parents. ⁸_____ names are Lucy and Stephen.'

'This is ⁹_____ dog. He's a boy dog. ¹⁰_____ name is Spot.'

Giving personal information

4 ✴✴✴ Write the questions to complete the interview.

Interviewer	¹ _What's your name?_
Oliver	Oliver Gerrard.
Interviewer	² _____
Oliver	I'm twelve.
Interviewer	³ _____
Oliver	Fifty-one, Baker Street.
Interviewer	⁴ _____
Oliver	It's 0243 87239.
Interviewer	⁵ _____
Oliver	Yes, it's oliver@xyz.co.uk.
Interviewer	Thank you.

can / can't

5 ⁑ **Look at the table and complete the sentences.**

	🎸	🎹	🐴	🏒
Sam	✓	✗	✗	✓
Anna	✓	✓	✓	✗

1 Sam _can play_ the guitar _but he can't play_ the piano.

2 Anna _____ the guitar _____ the piano.

3 Sam _____ a horse _____ ice hockey.

4 Anna _____ a horse _____ ice hockey.

Prepositions of place / Wh- questions

6 ⁑ **Complete the questions with How many, What or Where.**

1 _How many_ people are there?
There are two people.

2 _____ dogs are there?
There are two dogs.

3 _____ are they?
They're in the garden.

4 _____ colour is the ball?
It's white.

5 _____ is the ball?
It's in a tree.

6 _____ is the girl wearing?
She's wearing jeans and a T-shirt.

7 ⁑⁑ 🎧 1.2 **Listen to a description of a picture and choose the answers to the questions.**

1 How many people are there in the picture?
  a two   b three   c four

2 Where are they?
  a at school   b at a café   c at home

3 How many tables are there?
  a four   b two   c five

4 What are they wearing?
  a jeans   b dresses   c coats

5 What colour is the bag?
  a blue   b brown   c black

6 Where is the bag?
  a on a chair   b next to a chair
  c under a chair

have got / has got

8 ⁑⁑⁑ **Complete the questions and answers.**

Ben's bag   Mike's bag
Kate's bag   Lee's bag

1 ___Has___ Ben ___got___ a drink in his bag?
  Yes, he has.

2 How many sandwiches _____ Ben _____ in his bag?
  _____

3 _____ Ben _____ a pen in his bag?
  _____

4 How many keys _____ Kate _____ in her bag?
  _____

5 _____ Kate _____ a mobile phone in her bag?
  _____

6 _____ Kate _____ a watch in her bag?
  _____

7 _____ Mike and Lee _____ a drink in their bags?
  _____

1 My life

1A My daily life

Ordinal numbers

1 ★★ Write the ordinal numbers in words in the correct row.

1̶	2	3	5	10	12	20	21	22	30	31	40	43

-st	*first*		
-nd			
-rd			
-th			
-ieth			

My life

2 ★ Complete the text. Write the words for the pictures.

Hi! I'm Stella Phillips. I'm twelve and I live in Brighton. I'm in Year 8 at West Park Secondary School. My favourite subjects are ¹___*Maths*___ and ²_____. I don't like ³_____. I take the ⁴_____ to school. My brother comes, too. He goes to the same school, but he's in Year 9. We meet our friends at ⁵_____. School starts at ⁶_____, and finishes at ⁷_____.
After school, on Wednesdays, I play ⁸_____ and on Fridays I go ⁹_____. I have a ¹⁰_____ lesson on Tuesdays. After that, I go home and read a ¹¹_____.
I do my homework in the evening. My friends live in the same street, so they come to my house on Friday or Saturday evenings and we watch ¹²_____ together.

3 ★★ Read the text in exercise 2 again. Are the statements true (✓) or false (✗)? Correct the false ones.

1 Stella goes to a primary school.   ☒
   She goes to a secondary school.

2 She's in Year 10.   ☐
   _____

3 Her brother is in the same class.   ☐
   _____

4 They go to school by bus.   ☐
   _____

5 She likes Maths and Science.   ☐
   _____

6 She doesn't like History.   ☐
   _____

7 She plays tennis on Fridays.   ☐
   _____

8 She doesn't play a musical instrument.   ☐
   _____

4 ★★★ 🎧 1.3 Listen and answer the questions.

1 What floor do John and Stella live on?
   They live on the fourth floor.

2 What is John's favourite subject at school?
   _____

3 What time does his piano lesson start?
   _____

4 What time does his piano lesson finish?
   _____

5 What does John do on Fridays?
   _____

6 When do John and his friends play music together?
   _____

Present simple

5 ✱✱✱ **Look at the pictures and correct the information. Use the verbs in brackets.**

1 Harry gets up at seven o'clock. (get up)

Harry doesn't get up at seven o'clock. He gets up at
half past seven.

2 Harry walks to school. (walk / take)
_____
_____

3 Harry likes Maths. (like)
_____
_____

4 After school, Harry plays tennis. (play / go)
_____
_____

5 Harry's friends play computer games. (play / watch)
_____
_____

6 Harry's parents get home at half past five. (get)
_____
_____

Writing

6 ✱✱✱ **Look at the information in brackets and write affirmative and negative sentences about you and your friend.**

About me

1 (get up – time)
  I get up at ...
  I don't get up at ...

2 (leave home – time)
_____
_____

3 (play – sports)
_____
_____

4 (like – school subjects)
_____
_____

5 (go – extra lessons or activities)
_____
_____

About my friend

6 (live – where)
_____
_____

7 (go to school – how)
_____
_____

8 (like – school subjects)
_____
_____

9 (do homework – time)
_____
_____

10 (play – sports)
_____
_____

Months

1 * Write the months.

1 eDcebrme _December_

2 nurJaay _____

3 tAgusu _____

4 bmeSpetre _____

2 ** Complete the crossword with the months.

Dates

3 ** Complete the chart.

We write	We say
1 May	[1] _the first of May_
[2] _____	the fifteenth of October
3 April	[3] _____
[4] _____	the thirty-first of July
22 September	[5] _____
[6] _____	the eighteenth of January
9 February	[7] _____
[8] _____	the twentieth of June
12 August	[9] _____
[10] _____	the fifth of November

4 ** When are their birthdays? Write the dates in full.

1 Amy's _birthday is on the fourth of July_. (4/7)

2 Harry's _____

_____. (15/1)

3 Diana's _____

_____. (23/8)

4 Damian's _____

_____. (1/2)

5 Paul's _____

_____. (3/3)

6 Jack's _____

_____. (8/10)

7 Stephanie's _____

_____. (21/4)

8 Melanie's _____

_____. (5/12)

5 ✸✸✸ **Look at the calendar and answer the questions.**

JULY						
MON	TUES	WED	THURS	FRI	SAT	SUN
1	2	3	4	5	6	7
8	9	10	11	12	13	14
15	16	17	18	19	20	21
22	23	24	25	26	27	28
29	30	31				

1 Is the thirtieth of July a Monday?

No, it isn't. It's a Tuesday.

2 What day is the seventeenth?

_____

3 What date is the first Saturday in July?

_____

4 What date is the third Friday?

_____

5 What days are the tenth and the sixteenth?

_____

6 What day is the fourth day in July?

_____

7 What dates are all the Sundays on?

_____

8 What date is the last day of the month?

_____

9 Is the twenty-first of July a Sunday?

_____

10 What day is the thirteenth?

_____

6 ✸✸ 🎧 1.4 **Listen to five people and write the dates of their birthdays. Write sentences.**

1 *Elaine's birthday is on 14 May.*

2 _____

3 _____

4 _____

5 _____

Present simple

1 ★ This is Casey. He's from the USA. Some children are asking him about Thanksgiving. Complete the questions with *do* or *does*.

1 What __do__ children in the USA do on Thanksgiving Day, Casey?

2 _____ you go to school?

3 _____ your mum do all the cooking?

4 What _____ your dad do to help her?

5 What time _____ you have dinner?

6 _____ you watch TV in the evening?

7 _____ people give presents on Thanksgiving?

2 ★★ Write the words in the correct order to make questions.

1 Lisa / does / live / Where

__Where does Lisa live_____?

2 get up / time / does / What / she

_____?

3 go to / time / work / parents / do / What / her

_____?

4 play / does / sports / What / Lisa

_____?

5 Maths / Lisa / Does / like

_____?

6 do / do / on Saturdays / Lisa / What / and her friends

_____?

3 ★★ 🎧 1.5 Listen to Lisa and answer the questions from exercise 2.

1 She lives in _____ __Leeds_____ .

2 She gets up at _____ .

3 They go to work at _____ .

4 She plays _____ .

5 _____ .

6 They _____ .

4 ★★ Complete the dialogues with the correct form of the verbs in brackets.

1 • Where __does__ your mum __work__ ? (work)
  ○ She works in London.

2 • _____ you and your sister _____ TV after school? (watch)
  ○ Yes. I _____ *Science World* and my sister _____ *Fun with Art*.

3 • What sports _____ you and your friends _____ ? (play)
  ○ David and I _____ tennis and Amy _____ football.

4 • _____ your parents _____ other languages? (speak)
  ○ My father _____ French and they both _____ English.

5 • _____ you and your sister _____ to the same school? (go)
  ○ No, she _____ to a primary school and I _____ to a secondary school.

6 • What time _____ your school _____? (finish)
  ○ My school _____ at half past three.

5 ✶✶✶ Use the pictures to make questions and answers about Brett.

1 • ___Does Brett live___ in France?
  ○ ___No, he doesn't. He lives in the UK.___
2 • _____ volleyball?
  ○ _____
3 • _____ Spanish?
  ○ _____
4 • _____ in a block of flats?
  ○ _____
5 • _____ at seven o'clock?
  ○ _____

6 ✶✶✶ Look at the pictures and write the questions and answers.

1 • What sport / you play?
    ___What sport do you play?___
  ○ I ___play table tennis___.
2 • What musical instrument / your brother play?
    _____
  ○ He _____.
3 • What time / your school start?
    _____
  ○ It _____.
4 • What / you do in the evening?
    _____
  ○ I _____ and _____.
5 • How / your sister get to school?
    _____
  ○ She _____.
6 • What / your favourite school subject?
    _____
  ○ My _____.
7 • you / a pet?
    _____
  ○ Yes, _____.
8 • Where / you live?
    _____
  ○ We _____.

1D At home

Household jobs

1 ✱ **Match the words in A to the words in B.**

A	B
load	the bed
cook	the dishwasher
do	the floor
feed	the dinner
make	the cat
set	the recycling
take out	the shopping
tidy	the table
vacuum	the dog for a walk
take	your room

2 ✱✱ **Label the pictures with the expressions in exercise 1.**

1   *load the dishwasher*

2 _____

3 _____

4 _____

5 _____

6 _____

7 _____

8 _____

9 _____

10 _____

3 ✱✱ **Complete the text with the correct form of the verbs in exercise 1.**

In our house, we all have jobs. My father always ¹_____ *takes* _____ out the recycling. He puts it in the bins outside. My mother usually ²_____ the dinner, but I sometimes help her. I like making pasta! After dinner, I ³_____ the dishwasher. My mother ⁴_____ the shopping on Saturdays. I always ⁵_____ the dog. His name's Bobo and he's always hungry! I also ⁶_____ him for a walk before I go to school and when I come home. My brother ⁷_____ often _____ his room. My sister ⁸_____ her room every day!

4 ✱✱✱ 🎧 1.6 **Listen and write what jobs Toby does and doesn't do in the house.**

Things Toby does:
1   *He sets the table.*

2 _____

3 _____

4 _____

Things Toby doesn't do:
5   *He doesn't cook dinner.*

6 _____

7 _____

8 _____

Adverbs of frequency

5 ■ Write the words in the box in order of frequency.

> often   normally   not often
> sometimes   always   usually   ~~never~~

1 ____never____

2 _____

3 _____

4 _____

5 _____ and 6 _____

7 _____

6 ■■ Read the chart. Write five more sentences about the things Kristen does.

Tell us about yourself
How often do you ...?

	never	not often	sometimes	often	normally	always
1 forget someone's birthday			✓			
2 go on the Internet				✓		
3 play computer games	✓					
4 watch DVDs			✓			
5 do homework before school					✓	
6 tidy your room		✓				

1 _Kristen sometimes forgets someone's birthday._

2 _____

3 _____

4 _____

5 _____

6 _____

7 ■■■ Complete the sentences so that they are true.

About me:

1 I always _do my homework in the evening_ .

2 I never _____ .

3 I sometimes _____ .

4 I don't often _____ .

5 I usually _____ .

About other people (my mum, my brother, my best friend ...):

1 _My sister_ never _watches football on TV_ .

2 _____ sometimes _____ .

3 _____ doesn't often _____ .

4 _____ usually _____ .

5 _____ always _____ .

Progress check

1 **Complete the chart with the months of the year.**

Months	
1	*January*
2	
3	
4	
5	
6	
7	
8	
9	
10	
11	
12	*December*

2 **Write the dates how we say them.**

1 1/5

   the first of May

2 13/2

3 19/12

4 22/6

5 31/10

6 3/4

3 a 🎧 1.7 **Listen. Are the statements true (✓) or false (✗)?**

1 Luke and his friends are in the same class. ☒

2 Luke plays the drums. ☐

3 The teachers don't like the band's music. ☐

4 Sarah is good at French. ☐

5 Ed often cooks at Luke's house. ☐

6 Luke always sets the table. ☐

b 🎧 1.7 **Complete the questions about Luke and his friends. Then listen again and answer them.**

1 What school ___*do*___ they all go to?
   They _*all go to Northview Secondary School*_.

2 How _____ they get to school?
   They _____.

3 What instrument _____ Sarah play?
   She _____.

4 Where _____ they practise?
   They _____.

5 _____ the teachers like Luke's Maths?
   _____.

6 _____ Luke like PE and Geography?
   _____.

7 What subject _____ Ed know everything about?
   He _____.

8 What _____ they all love eating?
   They _____.

4 Put the words in the correct order to make sentences.

1 often / I / make my bed / don't
   I don't often make my bed.

2 vacuums / My mother / usually / the floor
   _____

3 loads / My dad / the dishwasher / normally / after dinner
   _____

4 a walk / the dog / never / for / My brother / takes
   _____

5 take out / We / the recycling / every day
   _____

6 sometimes / goes swimming / Craig / in the morning
   _____

5 Match the questions to the correct answers.

1 Do you like dogs?   `c`
2 Does your brother get up at seven o'clock?   ☐
3 Where does your mum work?   ☐
4 How many languages does your mum speak?   ☐
5 When do you do your homework?   ☐
6 When is your birthday?   ☐
7 How often does your dad cook?   ☐
8 Does your sister tidy her room?   ☐

a No, he doesn't.
b I do it in the evening.
c ~~Yes, I do.~~
d Never. He can't cook.
e Yes, she does.
f She works in London.
g Three. Italian, English and French.
h It's on 17 January.

I can …

Write the answers and tick (✓) the correct box.

1 I ¹_____ at

  ²_____ every day.

  At ³_____

  I ⁴_____ to school.

  What do you do at

  ⁵_____ on Saturday?

  I ⁶_____ .

I can talk and ask about daily activities and daily life.
☐ Yes   ☐ I need more practice

2 I never / often / sometimes
  _____ in my
  bedroom.
  But I never / sometimes /
  always _____ !

I can say how often I do things.
☐ Yes   ☐ I need more practice

3 Today is _____ .
  My birthday is on _____ .

I can say the date.
☐ Yes   ☐ I need more practice

2 Animals

2A Our school trip

Farm animals

1 * Circle the word which is a young animal.

1 dog / cat / (foal)
2 sheep / kitten / horse
3 puppy / pig / duck
4 cow / lamb / sheep
5 pig / kid / goat
6 calf / cat / dog

2 ** Write the words for the young animals.

1 a dog and a _puppy_
2 a cow and a _____

3 a cat and a _____
4 a duck and a _____

5 a horse and a _____
6 a pig and a _____

7 a sheep and a _____
8 a goat and a _____

Present continuous

3 * Read the sentences and draw the times on the clocks.

1 It is quarter past eleven. Matthew is swimming.
2 It is half past four. Kate is watching television.
3 It is ten o'clock. The children are walking.
4 It is half past one. Lisa and Debbie are running.
5 It is quarter to two. Russ and Mike are doing their homework.
6 It is half past ten. Tanya is eating a sandwich.

4 ✱✱ ◯ 1.8 **Listen to Martin and number the pictures in the correct order.**

a [ ]

b [ ]

c [1]

d [ ]

e [ ]

f [ ]

5 ✱✱ **Write the verbs in the correct column.**

1	~~go~~	4	get	7	run
2	have	5	write	8	cook
3	swim	6	eat	9	take

+ -ing	e + -ing	double last letter + -ing
going		

6 ✱✱✱ **Find five more differences between the pictures. Write sentences.**

1 In picture A, Mark *is swimming, but in picture B he's running*   .

2 In picture A, Alison _____
_____ .

3 In picture A, Natalie and Sara _____
_____ .

4 In picture A, Tim _____
_____ .

5 In picture A, Harry and Rob _____
_____ .

6 In picture A, Selina and Vicky_____
_____ .

2B Mickey's model dinosaur

Present continuous: questions

1 * **Complete the questions with *am*, *is* or *are*. Then match the answers (a–g) to the questions.**

1 ___*Is*___ Sally waiting for her friends? [c]
2 ________ I sitting on your sandwiches? [ ]
3 Where ________ your parents going? [ ]
4 ________ it raining? [ ]
5 ________ you making a model? [ ]
6 What ________ your dog eating? [ ]
7 ________ Leo playing a computer game? [ ]

a They're going shopping.
b Yes, I am.
~~c Yes, she is.~~
d No, he isn't. He's watching television.
e He's eating a bone.
f Yes, you are.
g No, it isn't.

2 a ** 1.9 **Listen and write the names next to the people in the picture.**

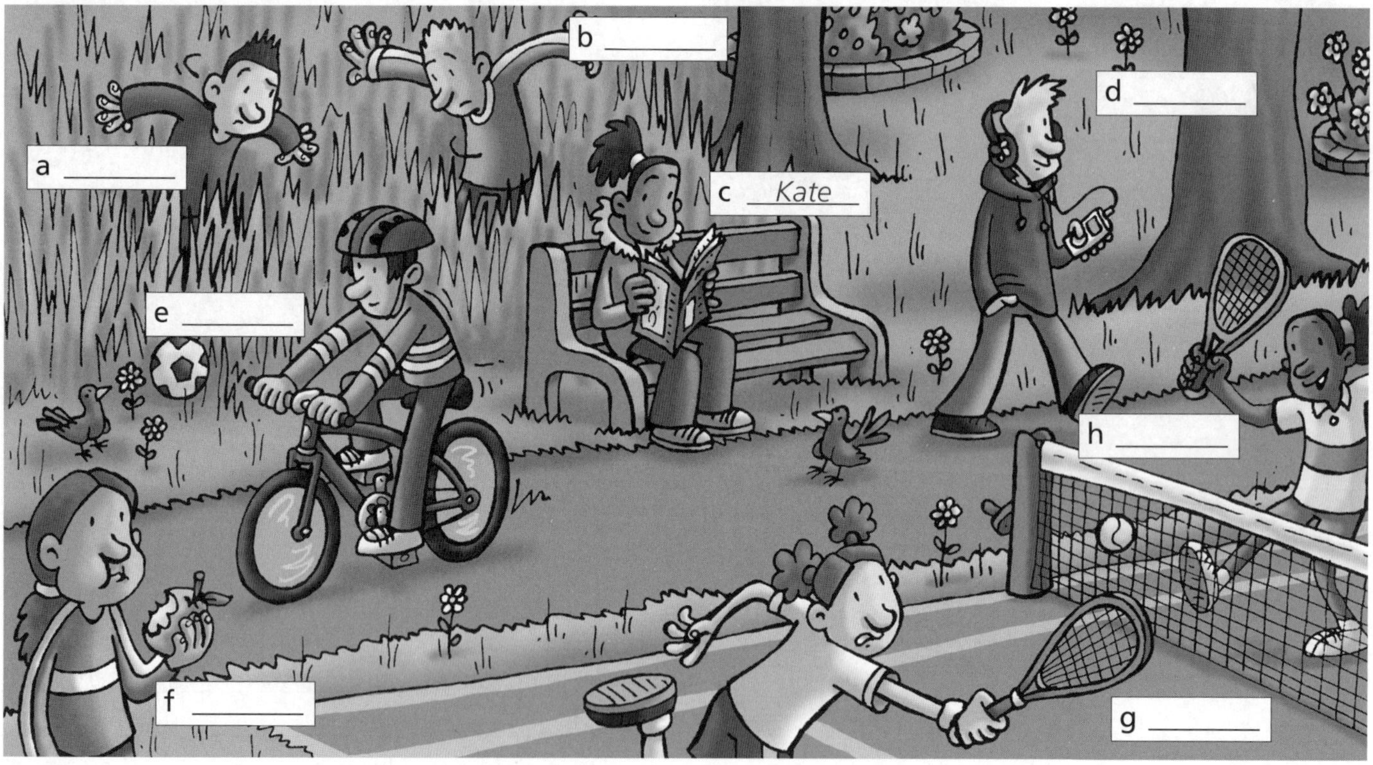

a ________
b ________
c *Kate*
d ________
e ________
f ________
g ________
h ________

b Answer the questions.

1 Is Kate reading?
Yes, she is.

2 What is Kate reading?
____

3 What is Ann doing?
____

4 Are Debbie and Sara playing tennis?
____

5 Is Dan playing a sport?
____

6 What is Ben doing?
____

7 Are Tom and David playing football?
____

8 What are Tom and David looking for?
____

3 ✱✱✱ **Complete Ellen's questions. Then write Neil's short answers.**

1 Ellen _____Are you drinking_____ juice? (you / drink)

  Neil _____No, I'm not._____

2 Ellen _____? (Joanna / dance)

  Neil _____

3 Ellen _____ funny clothes? (Simon / wear)

  Neil _____

4 Ellen _____?
  (Lewis and Joe / play with their band)

  Neil _____

5 Ellen _____? (Joanna's grandparents / watch)

  Neil _____

4 ✱✱✱ **Write questions for the answers. Use the present continuous tense.**

1 • _____Where are you going_____? (you / go)
  ○ I'm going to the park.

2 • _____? (Ewa / do)
  ○ She's doing a crossword.

3 • _____? (Steve / look for)
  ○ He's looking for the glue.

4 • _____? (Jill and Claire / make)
  ○ They're making a model.

5 • _____? (you / phone)
  ○ I'm phoning my friend.

6 • _____? (it / rain)
  ○ No, it isn't.

Writing

5 ✱✱✱ **Answer the questions about yourself.**

1 What are you wearing now?
  _____

2 What are your parents doing now?
  _____

3 Is your teacher talking now?
  _____

4 Where are you sitting now?
  _____

5 Are you listening to music now?
  _____

6 Is it raining today?
  _____

2C My favourite animals

Wild animals

1 ** Complete the crossword.

Across

Down

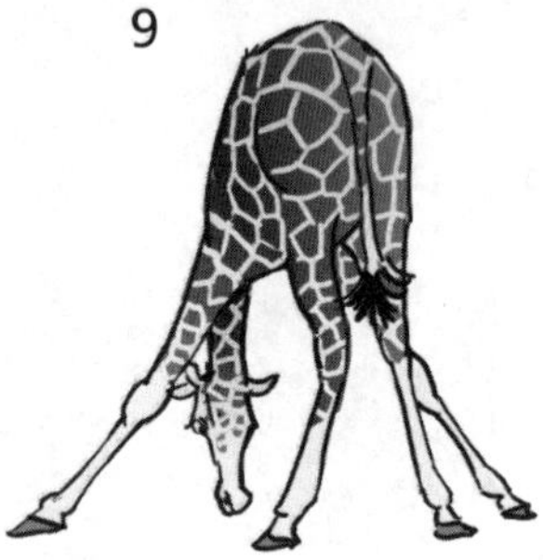

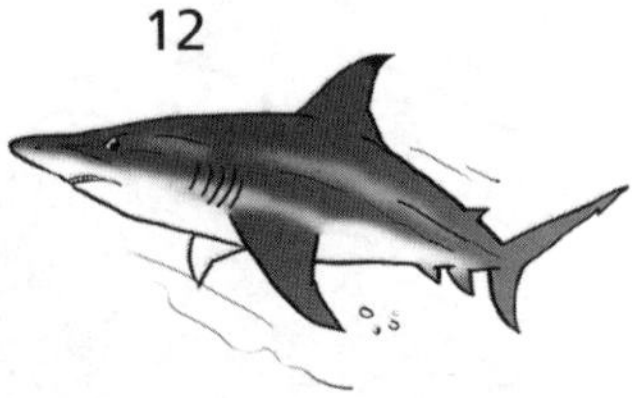

Make another animal from the special letters: __ __ __ __ __ __ __ __ __

2 ** Write the animals in exercise 1 in the correct column.
Some animals can go in more than one column.

They live on land	They live in water	They fly
a giraffe		

Present simple or present continuous?

3 ★★ 🎧 1.10 **Listen and complete the table.**

	usually	today
Fiona	[1] _does homework_	[2] _is writing emails_
Alex	[3] _____	[4] _____
Mum	[5] _____	[6] _____
Dad	[7] _____	[8] _____

4 ★★ **Complete the sentences.**

1 I _usually take_ the bus to school, but today _I'm walking_. (take / walk)

2 Sally _____ the monkeys' cage, but today _____ the giraffes. (clean / feed)

3 My mum and dad _____ shopping on Saturdays, but today _____ tennis. (go / play)

4 Alan _____ sandwiches for lunch, but today _____ a burger. (have / eat)

5 My friends and I _____ TV on Fridays, but today _____ to music. (watch / listen)

5 ★★★ **Read the dialogue. Write the names of the animals in the correct places.**

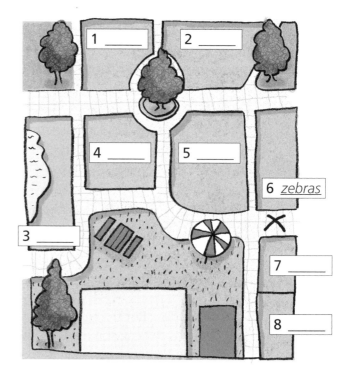

1 _____   2 _____
4 _____   5 _____
6 _zebras_
3 _____
7 _____
8 _____

Corinne	Oh, it's great at the zoo! Let's go and see the tigers first. Look at the map. Where are we now?
Hugh	Well, we're here, watching the zebras. The camels are next to the zebras and the tigers are behind the camels.
Corinne	OK. What can we see after the tigers?
Hugh	There are monkeys next to the tigers. We can see them and then we can walk to the kangaroos. They're between the camels and the crocodiles.
Corinne	Oh, I love crocodiles! What about the insect house? Where's that?
Hugh	The insects are behind us, next to the bats.
Corinne	OK, let's go!

Vocabulary

1 ✴⬛⬛⬛ **Label the pictures.**

1 _tree_ 2 _____ 3 _____ 4 _____ 5 _____ 6 _____ 7 _____ 8 _____

2 ✴✴⬛⬛ **Complete the story with the words opposite.**

One day an old woman makes a cake. It's a
¹ _gingerbread man_ ! The old woman takes the
cake out of the ²_____. But the gingerbread man
jumps up and runs away! 'Help,' the old woman
shouts. 'My gingerbread man is running away!' The
old woman runs after him. But she can't run fast.
The gingerbread man comes to a ³_____. He
stops because he can't swim. But a fox is sitting
there, under a big ⁴_____. 'Come with me. I can
swim very well,' he says. So the gingerbread man
jumps on his ⁵_____.
They swim across the river. But the fox is hungry
now. He says, 'You're very heavy on my back. Jump
on my ⁶_____.' The gingerbread man jumps on
the fox's head. Then the fox opens his ⁷_____
and eats the gingerbread man. So next time you
see a fox, don't listen to him!

gingerbread man

back

head

oven

mouth

river

tree

Subject and object pronouns

3 ✴✴⬛⬛ 🎧 1.11 **Listen to Terry. Choose the correct sentence.**

1 Paula and David are going to school.
   (She's waiting for him.)/ He's waiting for her.

2 I'm shopping with my parents.
   I'm looking for them. / They're looking for
   me.

3 Zara wants to play tennis. I'm there with her.
   I don't want to play tennis with her. / Zara
   doesn't want to play tennis with me.

4 My dad's talking on the phone to my mum.
   She often phones him. / He often phones her.

5 Paula and David are helping Zara and me with
   our homework.
   They often help us. / We often help them.

6 I'm going to school with my dad today.
   I don't often go to school with him. /
   He often goes to school with me.

4 ✱✱ Circle the correct word.

1 My best friend's name is Alison. I'm writing an email to **she** / **her** at the moment.

2 My mother loves birds. **She** / **Her** always reads books about **they** / **them**.

3 My aunt has got three cats. **I** / **me** always play with **they** / **them** when I go to her house.

4 This is my sister's horse, Lord. Lord likes **she** / **her** but he doesn't like **I** / **me**! He gets upset when I try to ride **he** / **him**!

5 Please, Dad, can you take **we** / **us** to the zoo again? There are two new baby bears there and **we** / **us** want to see **they** / **them**.

6 I don't understand this exercise. Can you help **I** / **me**, please?

must

5 ✱✱ Give advice. Use *must* and the words in the box.

| ~~learn the words~~   feed him   clean it |
| go to bed early   buy some at the shop   tidy it |

1 I've got a spelling test tomorrow.
You must learn the words.

2 I'm always tired in the morning.
_____

3 I can't find anything in my room!
_____

4 My dog isn't happy.
_____

5 I haven't got any glue for my project.
_____

6 My bike is dirty.
_____

6 ✱✱✱ What must Brad do for his dog, Prince? Make sentences with the verbs in brackets.

1 *He must feed Prince.* _____ (feed)

2 _____ (take)

3 _____ (wash)

4 _____ (play)

5 _____ (buy)

Progress check

1 **Circle the correct word.**

Which one …
1 is an insect?   a chicken / a duck / (a fly)
2 can't fly?   a budgie / an eagle / a shark
3 can fly?   a giraffe / a bat / a dolphin
4 can swim?   a shark / a cow / a goat
5 can climb a tree?   a monkey / a horse / a pig
6 eats insects?   a sheep / a goat / a frog
7 is a wild animal?   a sheep / a lion / a duck
8 is a farm animal?   a giraffe / a snake / a cow

2 **Find eight more animals in the wordsearch.**

H	H	E	O	Y	T	P	I	C	H	S
I	O	O	H	N	S	H	A	R	K	B
P	R	P	E	O	I	G	O	O	S	E
P	S	P	O	E	E	H	E	C	H	A
O	E	I	E	P	S	A	S	O	E	R
P	G	R	E	H	K	E	H	D	E	E
O	O	E	O	C	U	E	A	I	P	E
T	E	B	O	R	E	S	B	L	B	T
A	A	S	E	M	O	N	K	E	Y	M
M	G	E	P	L	O	L	Y	S	M	Y
U	L	I	O	N	P	H	O	R	I	A
S	E	L	E	P	H	A	N	T	P	S

3 **1.12** **Listen and number the animals in the order you hear them.**

cow   [ ]   duck   [1]
sheep [ ]   monkey [ ]
pig   [ ]   frog   [ ]
tiger [ ]

4 **Melanie works on a farm. Read the interview. Complete the questions and answers. Use the verbs in brackets.**

Interviewer	What ¹ _are you doing_ at the moment, Melanie? (do)
Melanie	I ²_____ the pigs' house. They aren't very tidy animals! (clean)
Interviewer	When ³_____ usually _____ them? (feed)
Melanie	They ⁴_____ their breakfast at seven o'clock in the morning and their dinner at five o'clock in the afternoon. (have)
Interviewer	What ⁵_____ the pigs _____ at the moment? (do)
Melanie	Well, that's the mother and her babies. She always ⁶_____ them. At the moment they ⁷_____. (watch / sleep)
Interviewer	What ⁸_____ the other pig over there _____? (do)
Melanie	It ⁹_____ for food. That is the daddy pig. He is always hungry. He ¹⁰_____ for his dinner. He loves dinner time! (look / wait)

5 **Change the words in brackets to** *me, he, him, it, she, them, they, us, we* **or** *you.*

- It's my brother's birthday today but ¹ *he* (my brother) isn't having a party.
- Why not?
- My mum and dad are taking ² _____ (my brother) to the cinema.
- My sister and I have got a hamster. ³ _____ (my sister and I) like ⁴ _____ (the hamster) very much.
- Do ⁵ _____ (you and your sister) clean it every week?
- I do. My sister doesn't. ⁶ _____ (My sister) doesn't help ⁷ _____ (I) at all.
- It's our class trip today. Our teacher, Mrs Bell, is taking ⁸ _____ (our class) to the zoo.
- I want to go to the zoo. I want to see the lions. ⁹ _____ (The lions) are my favourite animals. I love ¹⁰ _____ (lions).

6 **What must these people do? Write sentences with** *must.*

1 Johnny can't play the guitar very well. (practise more)

   He must practise more.

2 My sister always gets 1/10 for her tests. (do her homework)

   _____

3 My brother's hair is very long. (cut it)

   _____

4 My friends aren't quiet in class. (stop talking)

   _____

5 I can't see the board in class. (wear glasses)

   _____

6 We're going to the wildlife park. (bring cameras)

   _____

I can ...

Write the answers and tick (✓) the correct box.

1 The monkeys usually ¹ _____ the tree, but at the moment they ² _____. (climb / sleep)

I can talk about things that usually happen and things happening now.

☐ Yes   ☐ I need more practice

2 We're at the farm. I'm watching the ¹ _____. They are sleeping. Next to them, I can see a ² _____. The farmer is feeding it. In a field, two ³ _____ are running.

I can talk about animals.

☐ Yes   ☐ I need more practice

Don't forget!
- *practise the piano*
- *learn new English words*
- *buy Mum a birthday card*

3 I must ¹ _____. Then I ² _____. And it's Mum's birthday tomorrow. I ³ _____.

I can talk about the things I must do.

☐ Yes   ☐ I need more practice

3 Holidays

3A Where were you last weekend?

Phrases with *at*, *in*, *on*

1 ✱ **Label the pictures.**

1 on _h o l i d a y_

2 at a __ h __ __ __ __

__ __ __ __

3 at a __ __ __ __ __ i __ __

4 in __ __ d

5 on the __ __ __ c __

6 in the __ __ __ d __ __

2 ✱✱ 🎧 1.13 **Listen and complete the information about Pia's day.**

My birthday was last ¹_____Saturday_____. In the morning, I was at the ²_____ with my friends but it was raining so that wasn't fun. Later, we were at the ³_____.
The film was about ⁴_____. It was great! I was at home at quarter past ⁵_____ and there was a party. There were ⁶_____ people there. There was a cake and presents for me. I was very happy. I was in bed at half past ⁷_____. It was a great day!

was / were

3 ✱ **Complete the text with *was* or *were*.**

Last week, we ¹__were__ at the seaside. We ²_____ on holiday. The weather ³_____ very good. Our hotel ⁴_____ opposite the beach. The sea ⁵_____ lovely and warm. There ⁶_____ umbrellas on the beach. My brother and I ⁷_____ always in the sea, but my mum ⁸_____ usually in the sun! Next to the hotel, there ⁹_____ a lot of restaurants and cafés. The ice-creams ¹⁰_____ great! There ¹¹_____ twenty different ice-creams! My favourite ice-cream ¹²_____ the chocolate one. There ¹³_____ also a very interesting reptile park near our hotel. There ¹⁴_____ a big crocodile and there ¹⁵_____ a lot of snakes. They ¹⁶_____ horrible. The beach ¹⁷_____ the best place to go!

4 ★★ ☐ Where were they? Look at the pictures and correct the sentences.

1 Dana and Emily were at the zoo.

Dana and Emily weren't at the zoo. They were on the beach.

2 Andrew was at his sister's wedding.

_____
_____
_____
_____

3 Our teacher was at work.

_____
_____
_____
_____

4 We were at the cinema.

_____
_____
_____
_____

5 Martha was at the shops.

_____
_____
_____
_____

6 Sally and Josh were at a birthday party.

_____
_____
_____
_____

5 ★★★ Write questions and answers.

1 you / school / yesterday

• *Were you at school yesterday?*

○ *No, I wasn't. I was at the swimming pool.*

2 Sam and Dave / a birthday party / yesterday

• _____
_____

○ _____
_____

3 Tony / home / on Saturday

• _____
_____

○ _____
_____

4 Where / Adrian and Iza / last week

• _____
_____

○ _____
_____

5 your parents / at the zoo / last weekend

• _____
_____

○ _____
_____

6 Where / your teacher / last week

• _____
_____

○ _____

3B Our holiday

Going on holiday

1 * Label the pictures.

1 an _a i r p o r t_

2 a __ __ __ __ p __ __ __ __ __ __

3 a __ __ __ s __ __ __ __ __ __

4 a __ u __ __ __ __ __ __ __ __

5 __ __ g __ __ __ __ __

6 a __ __ __ b __ __ __

7 a __ __ __ __ l __ __ __ __

8 a __ __ __ __ t

Past simple

2 ** Complete the table with the past form of the verbs in the box.

| close practise study ~~book~~ play stop grab try arrive watch travel |

+ -ed	+ -d	double last letter + -ed	drop *y* + -ied
booked			

3 a ★★★ 🎧 1.14 **Listen to Jude and complete his diary for last week.**

Monday 11	practised ¹ *the guitar*
Tuesday 12	visited ² _____
Wednesday 13	watched ³ _____ at Simon's house
Thursday 14	played ⁴ _____ with Ian
Friday 15	tried to learn more ⁵ _____ words
Saturday 16	collected my ⁶ _____ for the school trip
Sunday 17	packed my ⁷ _____ for the trip

b Correct the sentences.

1 On Monday, Jude practised the piano.

   He didn't practise the piano.

   He practised the guitar.

2 On Tuesday, Jude visited his friend.

   _____

   _____

3 On Wednesday, Jude watched football at Simon's house.

   _____

   _____

4 On Thursday, Jude played tennis with Ian.

   _____

   _____

5 On Friday, Jude tried to learn more French words.

   _____

   _____

6 On Saturday, Jude collected his train ticket.

   _____

   _____

7 On Sunday, Jude packed his black suitcase.

   _____

   _____

4 ★★★ **Write about your last holiday. Write affirmative and negative sentences using the verbs.**

1 stay

   I stayed on a campsite.

   I didn't stay at a hotel.

2 visit

   _____

   _____

3 play

   _____

   _____

4 watch

   _____

   _____

5 try

   _____

   _____

6 pack

   _____

   _____

3C Holiday problems

Regular and irregular verbs

1 ✳ **Complete the crossword with the past form of the verbs.**

Across	Down
2 forget	1 steal
4 leave	2 feel
5 fall	3 get
7 bite	6 lose
8 take	7 break

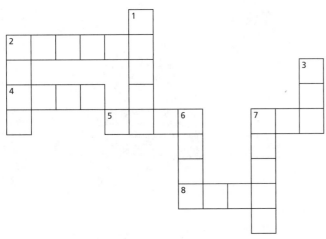

Past simple

2 ✳ 🎧 **1.15** **Listen to five people talking about holiday problems. Match the people (1–5) to the problems (a–e).**

1 Casey — `d`
2 Johnny — ☐
3 Tom — ☐
4 Tracey — ☐
5 Liz — ☐

a He / She felt ill.
b He / She broke his / her leg.
c He / She lost some money.
d ~~He / She missed a train.~~
e He / She dropped a camera.

3 ✳✳ **Put the verbs in brackets into the correct form. Then number the pictures in the correct order.**

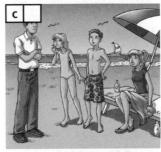

1 Mum and dad _packed_ (pack) the suitcases. Susie and I _didn't help_ (not help) them.

2 We _____ (say) goodbye to our dog. He _____ (not come) with us. He _____ (stay) at home with my grandma.

3 We _____ (get) to the airport at ten o'clock. We _____ (not miss) our plane. The plane _____ (leave) at twelve o'clock.

4 Mum and dad _____ (sleep) on the plane. Susie and I _____ (not sleep). We _____ (play) games.

5 We _____ (arrive) at our hotel at six o'clock in the evening. We _____ (not go) out. We were tired.

6 We _____ (go) to the beach. Dad _____ (not have) his swimming trunks. He _____ (forget) to pack them.

4 ★★ Natalie and Adam went on holiday last week. But their holidays were very different! Write sentences about them.

	Natalie	Adam
1		
2		
3		
4		
5		

1 (go by plane / not go by plane / go by boat)
Natalie *went by plane* .
Adam *didn't go by plane* .
He *went by boat* .

2 (stay at a hotel / not stay at a hotel / stay in a tent)
Natalie _____ .
Adam _____ .
He _____ .

3 (take lots of photos / not take lots of photos / break his camera)
Natalie _____ .
Adam _____ .
He _____ .

4 (write postcards / not write postcards / write emails)
Natalie _____ .
Adam _____ .
He _____ .

5 (enjoy her holiday / not enjoy his holiday)
Natalie _____ .
Adam _____ .

5 ★★★ Complete Spy 009's report by changing the verbs to the past simple.

SECRET DOCUMENT

Instructions for Spy 009

On Tuesday 13 February, at eight o'clock, take the train from Stansted Airport to Liverpool Street station in London. When you arrive, collect a ticket to Ipswich. Then wait under the clock. Look for a woman with a black umbrella. When she arrives, go with her to the café. Check the time and at twelve o'clock phone Doctor Strange. Leave the station and take a taxi to Euston. Go to the Belleview Hotel and collect the next instructions. Read them and then eat them.

Report by Spy 009

On Tuesday 13 February, at eight o'clock, I took the train from Stansted Airport to Liverpool Street station in London. When I ...
_____
_____
_____
_____
_____
_____

3D Mut's holiday

Holidays

1 ✳━━ 🎧 1.16 **Listen to Lucy and complete her email.**

○○○

Dear Helen,
We are on holiday in ¹ _Croatia_ . We arrived on
² _____ at ten o'clock in the evening. I was
very tired and sad because Sandy, my dog,
wasn't with me. We left Sandy with our
³ _____ , Mr Jackson. Then we drove our car
to the airport and took a plane.
We are staying at a campsite right next to the
⁴ _____ . There's a picture of it in this email.

At night, we sleep in a ⁵ _____ ! I like it but
mum and dad don't!
The weather is good – sunny and ⁶ _____ .
We go swimming every day. I brought my
camera with me, so I can show you some
photos when I come home.
Bye!
Love from Lucy

Past simple: questions

2 ✳━━ **Match the questions to the answers.**

1 Were you on holiday last week?   [d]
2 Where did you go?   ☐
3 How did you travel there?   ☐
4 Where did you stay?   ☐
5 Did you take your dog with you?   ☐
6 Who looked after him?   ☐
7 What did you do in Rome?   ☐
8 What did you like best?   ☐

a In a hotel.
b The food!
c No, we didn't.
d Yes, we were.
e We visited the Colosseum.
f To Rome.
g Our friends.
h By train.

3 ✳✳━ **Complete the questions for the answers.**

1 _Where did you go on holiday_ ?
   I went to New York.
2 _____ with?
   I went with my parents and my brother.
3 _____ ?
   We stayed at my aunt's house.
4 _____ ?
   We saw the Statue of Liberty and Central Park.
5 _____ ?
   I bought some jeans and a T-shirt.
6 _____ ?
   I ate lots of burgers and hot dogs.
7 _____ ?
   Yes, I had a great time!
8 _____ ?
   We got home last Saturday.

4 ✶✶✶ Write questions and short answers.

1 go / Paris?

Did you go to Paris?

No, I didn't.

2 travel / plane?

_____

_____

_____

_____

3 stay / hotel?

_____

_____

_____

4 buy / anything?

_____

_____

_____

5 like / the food?

_____

_____

_____

6 swim / the sea?

_____

_____

_____

5 ✶✶✶ Read Martha's mum's note. Martha didn't do everything on the note. Write the questions her mum asks when she gets home. Then write Martha's answers.

> ## Don't forget!
>
> Finish your homework ✓ 8 o'clock
> Feed the cats ✓
> Practise the piano ✗
> Pack your suitcase ✗
> Have something to eat ✓ a sandwich
> Look after Kieran! ✓ played games

1 • _Did you finish_ _____ your homework?
  ◦ _Yes, I did._ _____

2 • When _____ it?
  ◦ _____

3 • _____ the cats?
  ◦ _____

4 • _____ the piano?
  ◦ _____

5 • _____ your suitcase?
  ◦ _____

6 • What _____ to eat?
  ◦ _____

7 • What _____ you and Kieran do?
  ◦ _____

Writing

6 ✶✶✶ Martha is writing her diary about what she did today. Complete the diary with the information from exercise 5.

> Mum and Dad went out this evening. They left me a note with lots of things to do on it. I didn't do everything!
> First, I finished my homework ...

_____

_____

_____

_____

Progress check

1 Label the pictures.

1 _a boat_   2 _____

3 _____   4 _____

5 _____   6 _____

7 _____   8 _____

9 _____   10 _____

2 Complete the dialogue with *was* or *were*.

Donna   ¹ _Were_ you at home yesterday evening?
Nick   No, I ² _____ at the cinema.
Donna   ³ _____ your parents with you?
Nick   Yes, they ⁴ _____.
Donna   ⁵ _____ the film good?
Nick   Yes, it ⁶ _____ great!

3 Write the past form of the verbs in the box in the correct column.

> eat   miss   walk   watch   go   ~~be~~   drive
> forget   have   leave   lose   take   break
> shout   phone   play   come   swim   ~~arrive~~

Regular verbs	Irregular verbs
arrived	was / were

4 Use the past form of verbs from exercise 3 to complete Amelia's blog.

Posted on: Monday, 14 May

On Friday I ¹ _had_ a bad day. I ² _____ late for school, because I ³ _____ the bus. The teacher ⁴ _____ at me, because I ⁵ _____ to do my homework. And I ⁶ _____ my sandwiches at home! So I ⁷ _____ very hungry all day.

On Saturday, we ⁸ _____ to the beach.

We ⁹ _____ in the sea and ¹⁰ _____ wonderful food. Later, I ¹¹ _____ a football match on TV.

Yesterday I ¹² _____ the train to the cinema but I ¹³ _____ my ticket. I ¹⁴ _____ my dad and he ¹⁵ _____ in his car. He ¹⁶ _____ me back home.

5 **(1.17)** Listen to Adrian talking about his holiday. Did he do all of these things? Write Y (Yes) or N (No). Then write sentences about his holiday.

1	Travel by plane	N
2	Stay in a hotel	
3	Like the food	
4	Go to the beach	
5	Break his camera	
6	Lose his money	
7	Write postcards	
8	Enjoy his holiday	

1 _He didn't travel by plane._
2 _____
3 _____
4 _____
5 _____
6 _____
7 _____
8 _____

6 Complete the questions.

1 • When _did you go swimming_ ?
   ◦ I went swimming on Friday afternoon.
2 • How _____?
   ◦ I went there by bus.
3 • Who _____?
   ◦ I saw Melanie there.
4 • What _____ after that?
   ◦ We went to a restaurant for a pizza.
5 • _____ it?
   ◦ Yes, we liked it very much.
6 • When _____?
   ◦ We got home at eight o'clock.

I can ...

Write the answers and tick (✓) the correct box.

1 Last year I went on holiday to Brighton. We travelled by
   1 _____.
   We stayed in a
   2 _____.

I can say what I did on holiday.
☐ Yes   ☐ I need more practice

2 • Did you go swimming last Friday?
   ◦ No, I 1_____. And I 2_____
     (not see) my friends, because they
     3_____ (not be) at home.

I can say what I didn't do in the past.
☐ Yes   ☐ I need more practice

3 Where / go on holiday last month?
   1 _____
   travel / by train?
   2 _____
   When / arrive?
   3 _____
   What / do there?
   4 _____
   have / a good time?
   5 _____

I can ask about things people did in the past.
☐ Yes   ☐ I need more practice

4A Food and drink

Types of food and drink

1 ✱ Circle the food which is different.

1 lemonade tea (eggs) coffee
2 tuna chicken lamb pork
3 satsumas bananas salmon grapes

4 tomatoes beef lettuce beans
5 orange juice cheese pasta rice

2 ✱ Write the foods from exercise 1 in the correct column.

Meat	Fish	Fruit	Vegetables	Other	Drinks
				eggs	

3 ✱✱ Look at what three people usually eat for lunch. Complete the texts.

Hannah

Becky

Gary

I usually have two ¹e*ggs*_____ and two ²s_____. I love them with cheese and ³t_____. I always have ⁴t_____ to drink.

For lunch I often have a ⁵s_____ and lots of ⁶f_____. I like ⁷a_____, ⁸b_____ and ⁹o_____. I also have ¹⁰l_____ to drink.

I usually have a big lunch. I love ¹¹c_____ with ¹²b_____ and ¹³r_____. I don't like tea or coffee. I usually drink ¹⁴o_____ j_____.

Ordering food

4 ✶✶ 🎧 1.18 **Ed and Penny are ordering lunch. Listen and write what they order.**

Penny: Meat / Fish: 1 _chicken_
Vegetables / other: 2 _____
Drink: 3 _____

Ed: Meat / Fish: 4 _____
Vegetables / other: 5 _____
Drink: 6 _____

Penny: Dessert: 7 _____

Ed: Dessert: 8 _____

Countable and uncountable nouns

5 ✶ **Write the underlined food items in the correct column.**

Let's make lunch!

Chicken, rice and salad

You need:

200 g <u>beans</u>
2 <u>tomatoes</u>
2 <u>eggs</u>
<u>lettuce</u>
200 g <u>chicken</u>
350 g <u>rice</u>

Fruit salad

<u>bananas, apples,
oranges, grapes</u>

Drinks

<u>lemonade, water</u>

Countable nouns	Uncountable nouns
beans, _____,	_lettuce_, _____,
_____, _____,	_____, _____,
_____, _____,	

a / an

6 ✶✶ **Look at the picture. Complete the text with a, an or –.**

We're having a picnic! We've got 1 ___–___ pasta and 2 _____ cheese. There are 3 _____ sandwiches, there is 4 _____ chicken and there's 5 _____ big chocolate cake. And there's 6 _____ big salad. We put 7 _____ egg (only one), 8 _____ lettuce and 9 _____ tomatoes in it. To drink, we've got 10 _____ cola and 11 _____ lemonade. And there is 12 _____ fruit, too. We've got 13 _____ bananas, apples and 14 _____ orange.

Writing

7 ✶✶ **What do they want to eat and drink? Make sentences.**

Annie – beef, rice, banana
Charlie – cheeseburger, chips, apple
Dean – sandwich, satsumas, cola
Liam – chicken, beans, lemonade
Vicky – spaghetti Bolognese, orange, tea

1 Annie wants _beef, rice and a banana_.
2 Charlie wants _____.
3 Dean wants _____.
4 Liam wants _____.
5 Vicky wants _____.

4B Stone soup

Types of food and drink

1 ⬛⬛⬛ Complete the crossword.

Across

3   4

6   7   9

10   12

Down

1   2   5

8   9

10   11

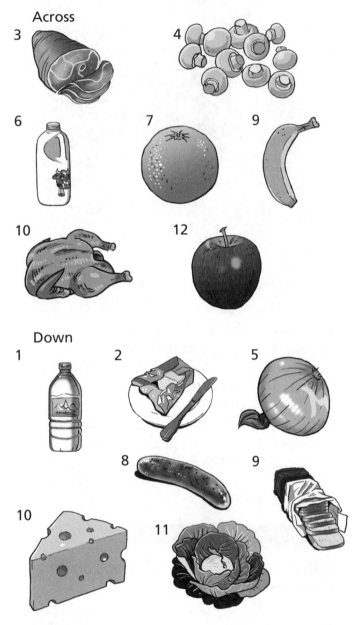

2 ⬛⬛⬛ Write the words from exercise 1 in the correct column.

Meat	Fruit	Vegetables	Drinks	Other
ham				

Crossword grid: 1 w / a / t / e / r (across 3 water)

a / an, some

3 ⬛⬛⬛ Circle the correct word.

1 I'd like a / **some** water, please.

2 Can I have **an** / some apple, please?

3 Carole usually has a / some ham sandwich for lunch.

4 My mum often cooks a / some beef for our Sunday dinner.

5 Can I have **an** / some egg for breakfast, please?

6 My brother likes pasta with a / some cheese.

7 Ben had a / some big chocolate cake for his birthday.

8 We've got **some** / an onion, a / some tomato and a / some ham here.

9 There are a / some mushrooms and **an** / some onions in this spaghetti Bolognese.

10 There's a / some bread and a / some butter here. We can make a / some sandwiches.

some and any

4 * 🔊 1.19 **Listen to William and his mother. Tick (✓) the things they have got and cross (X) the things they haven't got.**

orange juice ✓
bread X
ham
butter
milk
coffee
yoghurt
sugar

5 ** **Answer the questions about what William's family have and haven't got.**

1 • Have they got any juice?
  ○ _Yes, they've got some juice._

2 • Have they got any bread?
  ○ _No, they haven't got any bread._

3 • Have they got any ham?
  ○ _____

4 • Have they got any butter?
  ○ _____

5 • Have they got any milk?
  ○ _____

6 • Have they got any coffee?
  ○ _____

7 • Have they got any yoghurt?
  ○ _____

8 • Have they got any sugar?
  ○ _____

6 *** **Has Dominika got a healthy lunch? Complete the text with *some*, *any*, *a* or *an*.**

HAVE A HEALTHY LUNCH!

Healthy things
• a sandwich with chicken
• cheese
• fish
• fruit (apples, bananas, oranges)
• salad
• pasta or rice
• water or fruit juice

Unhealthy things
• cola, lemonade
• sweets
• crisps
• chips

Dominika hasn't got [1]___a___ chicken sandwich. She's got [2]_____ hamburger with [3]_____ chips. That's not very good for lunch! But Dominika has got [4]_____ cheese and [5]_____ fruit. She hasn't got [6]_____ apples or bananas, but she's got [7]_____ orange. She hasn't got [8]_____ pasta or rice and she hasn't got [9]_____ water. But she's got [10]_____ fruit juice. She hasn't got [11]_____ cola or lemonade today. She hasn't got [12]_____ sweets and she hasn't got [13]_____ crisps. She's got [14]_____ carrot. Dominika loves carrots!

4C Mut goes shopping

How much? / How many?

1 ✱ Put the things into the correct bag.

| dog food | lemons | water | onions |
| bread | salt | sausages | mushrooms |

How much?

1 _dog food_

2 _____

3 _____

4 _____

How many?

5 _lemons_

6 _____

7 _____

8 _____

2 ✱✱ Complete the questions.

1 • _How much_ chocolate do you eat a week?

○ I eat a bar of chocolate a week.

2 • _____ packets of crisps do you eat a week?

○ I eat three packets of crisps a week.

3 • _____ cola do you buy a week?

○ I never buy cola.

4 • _____ bread do you eat for breakfast?

○ I eat two slices of bread for breakfast.

5 • _____ water do you drink a day?

○ I drink about one litre of water every day.

6 • _____ pots of yoghurt do you eat a week?

○ I don't eat yoghurt. I don't like it.

Quantities

3 ✱ Label the pictures. Use the words in the box.

| a packet | a loaf | a carton | a tin |
| a bar | a pot | a bunch | a bag |

1 _a packet of crisps_

2 _____

3 _____

4 _____

5 _____

6 _____

7 _____

8 _____

4 ✱ ▬▬ Circle the correct word.

1 Can I have a kilo of (cheese)/ cheeses?

2 Kelly has got a **bunch** / **bar** of grapes for lunch.

3 How **much** / **many** loaves of bread are there in the shop?

4 How **much** / **many** cartons of milk do we need?

5 Do you want a **pot** / **tin** of yoghurt?

6 How **much** / **many** bread is there in the shop?

5 ✱✱ ▬ Find six more differences between the two pictures.

1 In picture A _there are two slices of bread_, but in picture B _there is one slice of bread_. (bread)

2 In picture A _____, but in picture B _____. (chocolate)

3 In picture A _____, but in picture B _____. (yoghurt)

4 In picture A _____, but in picture B _____. (bananas / grapes)

5 In picture A _____, but in picture B _____. (fish)

6 In picture A _____, but in picture B _____. (milk)

7 In picture A _____, but in picture B _____. (crisps)

6 ✱✱ 🎧 1.20 Rebecca is doing the shopping. Listen and complete her shopping list.

¹ _300 grams_ of ²_____

³_____ (big) ⁴_____

⁵_____

a small ⁶_____ of ⁷_____

a ⁸_____

Writing

7 ✱✱✱ Use the words to write a dialogue between Nick and a shop assistant.

1 Nick (have / you / bread)
   Have you got any bread?

2 Assistant (yes / how / you need)
   _____?

3 Nick (two / please)
   _____.

4 Nick (also / need / eggs)
   _____.

5 Assistant (sorry / we / not / got / eggs)
   _____.

6 Nick (have / you / apples)
   _____?

7 Assistant (yes / how / you want)
   _____?

8 Nick (want / two / apples / and / small bunch / bananas, please)
   _____.

4D Emma's apple crumble

Cooking instructions

1 ✱ **Label the pictures.**

1 m*ix*_____

2 p_____

3 p_____

4 b_____

5 s_____

6 f_____

2 ✱✱ **Complete the word puzzle.**

1 You boil potatoes in this.
2 You cook food in this.
3 You put soup in this to eat it.
4 You put food in your mouth with this.
5 You cut your food with this.
6 You eat soup with this.
7 You do this to cheese before you put it on your spaghetti Bolognese.

```
1 s  a  u  c  e  p  a  n
            2 o
         3     o
   4           k
      5        i
6              n
            7 g
```

3 ✱✱ 🎧 1.21 **Listen to the cooking instructions and number the pictures in the correct order.**

a ☐

b ☐

c ☐

d ☐

e ☐

f ☐ *1*

a / an, some, the

4 ✱✱◼ **Complete the text with a, an, some or the.**

How to make country style chicken

What do you need? ¹ _Some_ chicken, of course! And ² _____ potatoes and ³ _____ tin of tomatoes. You can use:

⁴ _____ onion (one is enough), ⁵ _____ red pepper (one whole pepper), ⁶ _____ mushrooms, ⁷ _____ big carrot and ⁸ _____ peas. And you need ⁹ _____ oil for frying. Oh, and don't forget ¹⁰ _____ large frying pan!

First, wash ¹¹ _____ vegetables. Then peel them with ¹² _____ knife. Chop ¹³ _____ chicken, onion, carrot and potatoes into small pieces. Boil ¹⁴ _____ potatoes and carrots in a saucepan and fry ¹⁵ _____ chicken. Then add ¹⁶ _____ onions, pepper and mushrooms to the chicken. You can then put in ¹⁷ _____ potatoes, carrots, peas and ¹⁸ _____ tin of tomatoes. Mix everything together and serve it on plates.

a little / a few

5 ✱◼◼ **Complete the sentences with a little or a few.**

1 I like pizza with ___ a little ___ ham and cheese.

2 There are _____ slices of chocolate cake on the table.

3 Can I have _____ butter on my potatoes?

4 Martin always has _____ bread with his soup.

5 Tara is making _____ pasta with _____ tomatoes and _____ cheese.

6 We need to buy _____ more cups and plates for our party.

6 ✱✱◼ **Circle the correct word.**

Ross   Let's make ¹(a)/ an chocolate cheesecake!

Julia   OK! Have we got ²a few / any chocolate?

Ross   Yes, there's ³a few / a little chocolate in the cupboard. How ⁴much / many do we need?

Julia   A lot, about two big ⁵tins / bars.

Ross   We haven't got enough. We can buy ⁶some / any.

Julia   And of course, we need ⁷a / some cheese, too.

Ross   We've got ⁸a few / a little cheese in the fridge. Look at the recipe. How ⁹much / many flour do we need?

Julia   About a cup. And we need ¹⁰a / some water. And what about ¹¹a / an egg? How ¹²much / many eggs do we need?

Ross   Two. We need ¹³some / any sugar and ¹⁴some / any butter. Oh, dear. We haven't got ¹⁵some / any sugar.

Julia   We can buy a ¹⁶bowl / bag of sugar in the shop, too.

Writing

7 ✱✱✱ **Write your own recipe. Write the ingredients and instructions.**

_____

_____

_____

_____

_____

_____

_____

_____

_____

_____

_____

_____

Progress check

1 Circle the correct word.

1 knife (fork) spoon
2 chicken salmon beef

3 carrots grapes satsumas
4 beans tomato lettuce

5 bread butter cheese
6 onions peas mushrooms

2 Write C for countable or U for uncountable.

1 tuna   _U_
2 onions   _____
3 lemonade _____
4 grapes   _____
5 chicken   _____

6 rice   _____
7 carrots   _____
8 cola   _____
9 bananas   _____
10 pasta   _____

3 Complete the questions with *much*, *many*, *is* or *are*.

1 How _much_ water _is_ there?
2 How _____ orange juice _____ in the bottle?
3 How _____ eggs _____ there?
4 How _____ bananas _____ there?
5 How _____ tea _____ there?
6 How _____ sandwiches _____ there?

4 Look at the picture. Write the answers to the questions in exercise 3. Use *some*, *any*, *a* or *an*.

1 There _isn't any_ water.
2 There _____ orange juice in the bottle.
3 There _____ eggs.
4 There _____ bananas.
5 There _____ tea.
6 There _____ sandwich.

5 🎧 1.22 Listen and match the people (1–8) to the pictures (a–h).

1 Angela   2 Ed   3 Melissa 4 Johnny
5 Barbara   6 Peter   7 Mary   8 Jack

a [ ]
b [ ]

c [ ]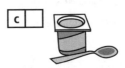
d [ ]

e [1]
f [ ]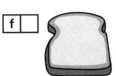

g [ ]
h [ ]

42

6 Complete the text with the words in the box.

cleaned ~~summer~~ mixed dropped bowl any some cakes spoon oven recipe ingredients butter kitchen

Fiona and Leo didn't have anything to do. It was their [1]_____summer_____ holiday but it was raining. 'What can we do today?' asked Fiona. 'We can make some [2]_____,' said Leo. 'There's a great [3]_____ in this magazine. We can make lemon cakes.'

'Have we got all the [4]_____?' asked Fiona. Leo looked in the cupboard. 'We've got flour and sugar, but we need some eggs and [5]_____.' 'Have we got [6]_____ lemons?' asked Fiona. 'There aren't any on the shelf,' said Leo. 'That's OK,' said Fiona. 'There are [7]_____ oranges on the table.'

They put the ingredients in a [8]_____. Leo [9]_____ them together with a [10]_____. They made fifteen cakes and put them in the [11]_____. 'We've got thirty minutes,' said Leo. 'We can play computer games.'

After an hour, Leo shouted, 'Oh no! Our cakes!' They ran to the [12]_____. Fiona opened the oven. She grabbed the dish, but it was hot and she [13]_____ all the cakes on the floor.

That afternoon, Fiona and Leo had lots of things to do. They loaded the dishwasher and [14]_____ the kitchen. But they didn't have any delicious orange cakes …

I can …

Write the answers and tick (✓) the correct box.

1 For breakfast,
[1] _I have a slice of bread,_
[2]_____ and [3]_____.

I can say what I eat.
☐ Yes ☐ I need more practice

2 Waitress [1] _Yes, please_ ?
Me [2]_____ I have tuna and a salad, [3]_____?
Waitress Is [4]_____ everything?
Me Yes, [5]_____.

I can order food in a restaurant.
☐ Yes ☐ I need more practice

3 • How [1]_____ apples have we got?
○ We've got a [2]_____ – about five or six.
• How [3]_____ butter have we got at home?
○ Only [4]_____ butter. We need more.

I can plan the shopping.
☐ Yes ☐ I need more practice

4 To make pancakes, you mix flour, eggs and butter. Then you [1]_____ the mixture into a [2]_____ and [3]_____ the pancakes.

I can say how to make my favourite food.
☐ Yes ☐ I need more practice

5A My country

The United Kingdom

1 ★ Rearrange the letters to make ten things, then find them on the map.

1 The New ____Forest____ (sorFet) is very beautiful.

2 Ben Nevis is a _____ (noamiutn).

3 Windermere is a _____ (akel).

4 The Severn is a _____ (ivrre).

5 The M1 is a _____ (owymrtoa).

6 The Isle of Man is an _____ (sdilna) between England and Ireland.

7 The Channel _____ (ulTnen) goes from England to France.

8 The Forth _____ (reiBgd) is in Scotland.

9 The Shard building is a _____. (akpscyesrr) in London.

10 Pendine Sands is a _____ (ecbah) in Wales.

2 ★★ Match the words from exercise 1 to the places on the map.

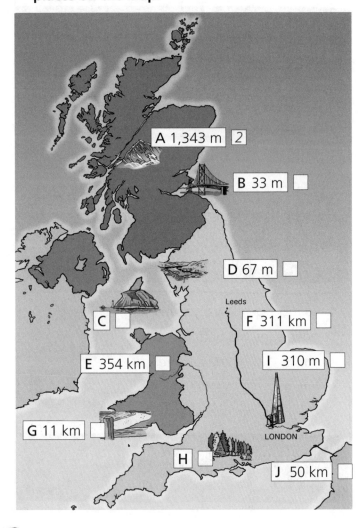

A 1,343 m ☐2
B 33 m ☐
D 67 m ☐
Leeds
C ☐
F 311 km ☐
E 354 km ☐
I 310 m ☐
G 11 km ☐
LONDON
H ☐
J 50 km ☐

How questions

3 ★★ Look at the map. Complete the questions and answers. Use the words in the box.

> deep   high   long   wide

1 How __long__ is the River Severn?
It's __354 km long__ _____.

2 How _____ is Ben Nevis?
It's _____.

3 How _____ is Lake Windermere?
It's _____ in the middle.

4 How _____ is the Shard skyscraper?
It's _____.

5 How _____ is the Channel Tunnel?
It's _____.

6 How _____ is the Forth Bridge?
It's _____.

7 How _____ is the M1 motorway?
It's _____.

4 ★★ 🎧 1.23 **Listen to someone talking about Loch Ness and answer the questions.**

1 How long is Loch Ness?

It's ____36 km____ long.

2 How wide is Loch Ness?

It's _____ wide.

3 How deep is Loch Ness?

It's _____ deep.

4 How many islands are there in the Loch?

_____

5 How high is Mealfurvonie?

It's about _____ high.

6 How long is the walk?

It's about _____ long.

5 ★★★ **Make full questions.**

1 wide / the Champs Elysees in Paris?

How wide is the Champs Elysees in Paris?

It's 70 metres wide.

2 high / Mount Etna in Sicily?

_____

It's 3,329 metres high.

3 What / GB / short for?

_____

It's short for Great Britain.

4 long / River Danube?

_____

It's 2,850 km long.

5 Where / Cardiff?

_____

It's in Wales.

6 Milan / big city?

_____

Yes, it is. It's a very big city.

7 deep / Lake Geneva?

_____

It's about 300 metres deep in some places.

8 long / the Interstate 44 road in the USA?

_____

It's 4,991.81 km long!

Writing

6 a ★★★ **Look at the information about The London Eye. Complete the text with one word in each gap.**

> ### Fact sheet:
>
> **Name:** The London Eye
> **Where:** London, next to River Thames
> **Facts:** 135 m high
>
> Opened: 9/3/2000
>
> 3.5 million visitors each year
>
> See from top: all of London
>
>
>
> This [1]____is____ The London Eye. It's [2]_____ London. It's next to the River Thames. It's 135 [3]_____ high. It opened [4]_____ 9 March 2000 and 3.5 million people [5]_____ the London Eye each year. [6]_____ the top, you can see all of London.

b Now write about the Eiffel Tower.

> ### Fact sheet:
>
> **Name:** The Eiffel Tower
> **Where:** Paris, next to River Seine
> **Facts:** 324 m high
>
> Opened: 31/3/1889
>
> Over 6 million visitors each year
>
> See from top: all of Paris
>
>
>
> This _____
>
> _____
>
> _____
>
> _____
>
> _____
>
> _____
>
> _____

The weather

1 * Label the pictures. Use the words in the box.

dry hot windy foggy cloudy
raining icy snowing sunny cold

1 _It's dry._

2 _____

3 _____

4 _____

5 _____

6 _____

7 _____

8 _____

9 _____

10 _____

2 ** Complete the crossword.

Across

1 → on a compass.

4 September, October and November are months in ...

5 The opposite of dry.

7 March, April and May are months in ...

8 ← on a compass

	¹E	A	²S	T		³
⁴						
			⁵			
⁶		⁷				
⁸						

Down

2 A great time of year to swim in the sea in Europe.

3 ↑ on a compass

5 A cold time of year in Europe.

6 When it is sunny and dry, we can say it is ...

7 ↓ on a compass.

Comparative adjectives

3 * Circle the correct word.

1 England is **bigger** / **smaller** than Wales.

2 London is **hotter** / **cooler** than Athens.

3 Mt Blanc is **shorter** / **higher** than Ben Nevis.

4 Holland is **flatter** / **wider** than Switzerland.

5 The Eiffel Tower is **higher** / **older** than the Tower of London.

6 The Thames is **longer** / **shorter** than the Nile.

4 ✱✱✱ 🎧 1.24 **Listen to the descriptions. Label the people with the correct names.**

Lisa	Anna	Kate	Eve	Pam

| 1 ____ | 2 ____ | 3 ____ | 4 ____ | 5 ____ |

5 ✱✱ **Complete the sentences with the comparative form of the adjectives in brackets.**

1 France is much _____smaller_____ than Canada. (small)

2 Who do you think is _____ – Jennifer Lopez or Angelina Jolie? (beautiful)

3 I am _____ in summer than in winter. (happy)

4 I think English is _____ than French. (difficult)

5 The south is much _____ than the north. (flat)

6 Antarctica is _____ than any other place in the world. (cold)

7 Parrots usually live _____ than dogs or cats. (long)

8 I think swimming in the sea is _____ than swimming in the pool. (nice)

6 ✱✱✱ **Write sentences. Make comparisons.**

1 long / short

Alison's hair _is longer than Lucy's_.   Lucy's hair _is shorter than Alison's_.

2 thin / thick

Mick's sandwich _____.   Harry's sandwich _____.

3 big / small

Duke _____.   Pongo _____.

4 wet / dry

Saturday was _____.   Sunday was _____.

5 quiet / crowded

The mountains _____.   The beach _____.

5C Record breakers

The world

1 ✱▨▨ **Write the names of the continents (1–7) on the map.**

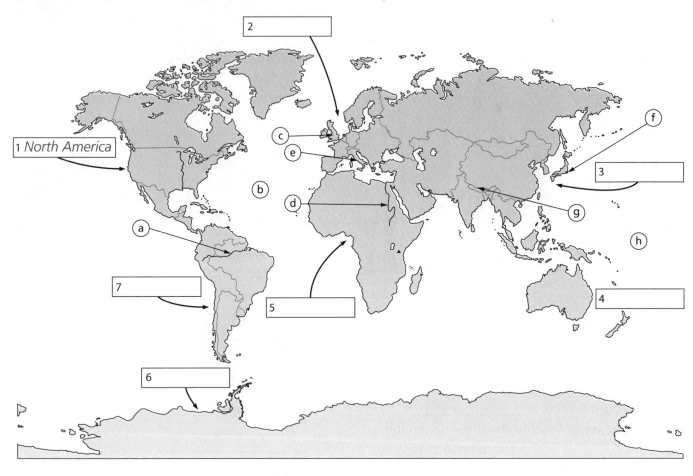

2 ✱✱▨ **Find the places on the map. Write the correct letters (a–h).**

- the Amazon — `a`
- Vatican City — ☐
- the Nile — ☐
- Tokyo — ☐
- Everest — ☐
- the Atlantic — ☐
- the UK — ☐
- the Pacific — ☐

3 ✱✱▨ **Write the places in exercise 2 with the correct descriptions.**

1 It's a river. _the Amazon, the Nile_
2 It's a country. _____
3 It's an ocean. _____
4 It's a capital. _____
5 It's a mountain. _____

4 ✱✱▨ **Look at the map again and answer the questions.**

1 Which continent is the largest?
  Asia
2 Which continent is the smallest?

  _____
3 Which island is the biggest in Oceania?

  _____
4 Which continent is south of Europe?

  _____
5 Which continent is the River Amazon in?

  _____
6 Is North America bigger or smaller than Europe?

  _____

Superlative adjectives

5 ★ ■ ■ **Put the adjectives in brackets into the superlative form.**

1 The _____*hottest*_____ capital city in Europe is Athens in Greece. (hot)

2 The _____ city in Europe is Zurich in Switzerland, but Copenhagen has more rainy days. (wet)

3 Zurich is also the _____ city in Europe. (expensive)

4 The _____ city in Europe is Lisbon but it isn't the _____. (sun / dry)

5 London has the _____ difference between the temperature in summer and the temperature in winter. (small)

6 Monaco is the _____ country in Europe. (crowded)

7 Milan is the _____ city in Europe. It has fog on 343 days of the year! (foggy)

8 Helsinki is the _____ capital city in Europe. It has 169 days a year when the temperature is below zero. (cold)

6 a ★★ ■ 🎧 1.25 **Listen and complete the information.**

	London	Madrid	Rome	Budapest
Population	7.8 million	3.2 million	2.8 million	2 _____ million
Hours of sun	3 _____	2,769	4 _____	1,933
Rain	5 _____ mm	436 mm	6 _____ mm	593 mm

b **Make sentences about the cities using the superlative form of the adjectives in brackets.**

1 *London is the biggest of the four cities.* (big)

2 _____ (small)

3 _____ (sunny)

4 _____ (wet)

5 _____ (dry)

Writing

7 ★★★ **Complete the questions about your country. Then try to answer them.**

1 What is _*the most popular*_ place for tourists to visit? (popular)

_____

2 What is _____ building? (old)

_____

3 Which city is _____? (beautiful)

_____

4 What is _____ shop in your town? (expensive)

_____

5 What is your country's _____ food? (delicious)

_____

6 Who is your country's _____ singer? (famous)

_____

7 What is _____ month in your country? (wet)

_____

8 What is _____ book by a writer from your country? (interesting)

_____

9 What is _____ building? (tall)

_____

10 What is _____ river? (long)

_____

as ... as

1 ** Complete the sentences with expressions using *as ... as*.

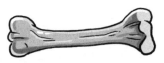

1 Come and sit by the fire! Your hands are _as cold as_ ice.

2 The puppy only weighs 500 g. It's _____ a feather.

3 It's raining, but we are _____ a bone inside our tent.

4 This new skyscraper is _____ a mountain!

5 He's an old man, with hair _____ snow.

6 Let's go swimming. It's _____ toast today.

7 This new train is _____ lightning.

8 Our new car has got seven seats. It's _____ an elephant!

9 There's a hole in our garden which is _____ the sea!

2 ** Look at the picture. Complete the crossword.

Guidebook

THE SEA 200 m 7

SEA VIEW 8

Comparatives and superlatives

3 a ** 🎧 1.26 **Listen and number the places in the correct order.**

	Sennen Beach	St Ives Beach	Praa Sands Beach
1 Longest	1	3	2
2 Most popular			
3 Best for swimming			

	Caravan	House	Hotel
4 Most expensive			
5 Most comfortable			
6 Most exciting			

b Complete the sentences.

1 Praa Sands is _____ *longer* _____ than St Ives beach, but _____ *the longest* _____ beach is Sennen.

2 Praa Sands is _____ than Sennen, but _____ beach is St Ives.

3 Praa Sands is _____ beach for swimming because it has the warmest water. St Ives is _____ for swimming than Sennen.

4 Houses are _____ than caravans, but _____ places to stay are hotels.

5 Hotels are _____ places to stay. Houses are _____ than caravans.

6 Hotels are _____ places to stay than houses, but _____ places to stay are caravans on big campsites.

4 ** **Complete the sentences with *better, the best, worse* or *the worst*.**

- Do you want a pizza?
- Yes, but not from here. The pizzas in here are ¹ *the worst* in the world.
- They're ² _____ than in Pizza Power.
- Oh yes. I forgot that restaurant. You're right. Pizza Power is ³ _____ than this place.
- So where's ⁴ _____ place for pizzas?
- Pete's Pizzas. They're delicious!

- You look happy.
- Yes. My project was ⁵ _____ in the school.
- Really? Was it ⁶ _____ than Joe's?
- Yes, it was. I was surprised because my last project was much ⁷ _____ than his. He usually does very good projects but this was ⁸ _____ one he's done this year.

Writing

5 *** **Make either a superlative sentence (S) or a comparative sentence (C).**

1 difficult (school subject)
   The most difficult school subject
   is Maths. (S)

2 interesting (place to visit in your country)
   _____ (S)

3 bad (pop group)
   _____ (C)

4 good (month of the year)
   _____ (C)

5 good (place to eat in your town)
   _____ (S)

6 funny (TV programme)
   _____ (C)

7 nice (place to go for a walk in your town)
   _____ (S)

8 big (city in your country)
   _____ (C)

Progress check

1 Write the answers.

1 North and South America are examples of c_*continents*_ .

2 China and Russia are examples of c_____.

3 The Atlantic is an example of an o_____.

4 Paris and London are c_____ cities.

5 The four points of a compass are:

_____.

6 Spring and summer are two of the s_____.
The two others are: _____.

7 The Amazon and the Nile are two long
r_____.

8 The highest m_____ in the world is
Everest.

9 A_____ is the coldest continent.

10 The Channel T_____ runs under the sea
from England to France.

2 Match the pictures to the sentences.

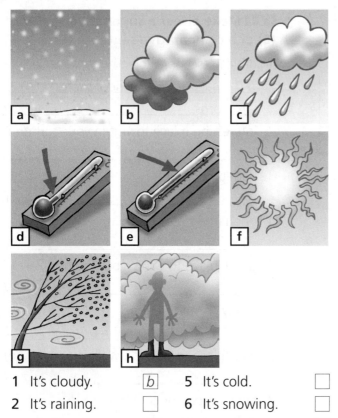

a	b	c
d	e	f
g	h	

1 It's cloudy. [b]   5 It's cold. [ ]

2 It's raining. [ ]   6 It's snowing. [ ]

3 It's foggy. [ ]   7 It's windy. [ ]

4 It's warm. [ ]   8 It's sunny. [ ]

3 Make full sentences.

1 She's got beautiful eyes. They / blue / sky.
*They're as blue as the sky.*

2 I've got all my books in my bag and I can't pick it
up. It / heavy / lead.

_____

3 I keep my books at school, so my bag isn't
heavy. It / light / feather.

_____

4 Don't touch me. Your hands / cold / ice.

_____

5 It's very sunny today and 20°C! It / warm / toast.

_____

6 David won the 100 metres race. He / fast /
lightning.

_____

4 Complete the sentences with the comparative or superlative form of the adjectives in brackets.

1 Amy and Donna are _*the friendliest*_ girls in
our class. (friendly)

2 James is _____ friend in the world.
(good)

3 A Rolex watch is _____ than a
Swatch watch. (expensive)

4 I think that _____ weather is in
summer. (nice)

5 Tom is _____ than Dan. But Luke is
_____ boy in our class. (tall)

6 It rained all day yesterday, but today the weather
is _____. (good)

7 Yesterday was _____ day of my life!
It was _____ than the day I broke
my arm! (bad)

8 Rome is _____ than London in the
winter but it is also _____.
(hot / wet)

5 🎧 1.27 Listen and complete the text.

PACIFIC OCEAN

Auckland

Lake Taupo

NORTH ISLAND

NEW ZEALAND

Wellington

Mount Cook

Christchurch

SOUTH ISLAND

Dunedin

I'm from New Zealand. There are only about ¹___*four*___ million people in my country.

There are more ²_____ than people here! New Zealand is one of the most ³_____ countries in the world.

There are two big islands. South Island is ⁴_____ than North Island, but the weather in North Island is better – it's ⁵_____ and sunnier. But it isn't sunny all the time. In winter it ⁶_____ a lot.

There are a lot of hills and high mountains in South Island. The highest is Mount ⁷_____. It's 3,754 metres high. The capital city is in the North Island. It's called ⁸_____.

I can ...

Write the answers and tick (✓) the correct box.

1 My favourite season is summer. The weather is usually ¹_____ and ²_____, and it doesn't ³_____ very often.

1

2

3

I can talk about the weather and seasons.

☐ Yes ☐ I need more practice

2 I think summer is ¹_____ (good) than winter. It is ²_____ (hot) and ³_____ (sunny). Winter is ⁴_____ (dark) and ⁵_____ (wet) than summer. But ⁶_____ (nice) season is spring!

I can compare different things.

☐ Yes ☐ I need more practice

3 The capital city of my country is ¹_____. The highest mountain is ²_____ and the longest river is ³_____. I think the most beautiful place in my country is ⁴_____.

I can talk about my country.

☐ Yes ☐ I need more practice

6 Entertainment

6A TV programmes

Types of TV programmes

1 ★★ **Match the programmes (1–9) to the descriptions in the TV guide (a–i).**

1 a quiz show   *i*
2 a soap opera   ☐
3 a cartoon   ☐
4 a police drama   ☐
5 a documentary   ☐
6 the news   ☐
7 a reality show   ☐
8 a comedy programme   ☐
9 a film   ☐

a Learn all about whales and dolphins in this great new programme.

b What is Mickey Mouse going to do this time? Watch all your favourites – *Tom and Jerry, Donald Duck,* ...

c It's a story about students at a wizard school, with Daniel Radcliffe as Harry, and Emma Watson as Hermione.

d Do you remember what happened last week? Jessica's boyfriend arrived, but she wasn't there ... Find out what happened to him in tonight's show!

e This is the funniest programme in the world!

f Who is going to leave the house this week? On this show, you have a chance to choose. Decide and phone us!

g They drive fast cars and catch robbers ... See what happens tonight in *Miami Cops.*

h Find out what is happening right now around the world.

i How much do you know? Try to answer these questions!

2 ★★ **Complete the dialogue with the words in the box.**

| show | opera | ~~TV guide~~ | record | interview | control |

Nick   Where's the ¹ *TV guide* ?

Amber I'm reading it. Oh great! My favourite soap ²_____ is on soon. Oh no! There's a good chat ³_____ on at the same time. They always ⁴_____ interesting people like film stars and pop stars.

Nick   You can ⁵_____ the soap opera and watch it later.

Amber Good idea. Can I have the remote ⁶_____?

Nick   Here it is.

3 ★★ 🎧 1.28 **Listen to two people talking about television programmes. Number them in the order they are going to watch them. There are two programmes that they aren't going to watch.**

a ☐ a sports programme
b ☐1 a cartoon
c ☐ a police drama
d ☐ a chat show
e ☐ the news
f ☐ a reality show
g ☐ a comedy programme
h ☐ a film

going to

4 ⬚■■■ **Complete the dialogue with *going to* and the verbs in brackets.**

Karina What ¹ *are we going to watch* (watch) on TV tonight?

Alec Well, I ²_____ (not miss) *The Simpsons* tonight. It's my favourite programme. Do you remember what happened last week?

Dad There's a football match on TV tonight. It starts at seven o'clock.

Karina Oh no! It ends at ten o'clock.
³_____ (you / watch) it all?

Mum No, he isn't! My favourite quiz show is on at eight o'clock. I ⁴_____ (watch) that. And you and your brother ⁵_____ (finish) your homework before you watch anything.

Karina OK, Mum. I don't mind. I ⁶_____ (record) *In the House*. It's my favourite reality show. I can watch it later.

Alec So, what about *The Simpsons*? Dad ⁷_____ (watch) the football, Mum ⁸_____ (see) her programme, Karina ⁹_____ (not miss) her reality show – what about me?

Dad Don't worry. I ¹⁰_____ (do) some work this evening. I don't really want to watch the football!

Alec / Karina Dad!

5 ■■■ **Read Paul's diary for next week. Complete the questions and answers.**

MONDAY	have a piano lesson
TUESDAY	revise for a test
WEDNESDAY	do the Science project
THURSDAY	watch The Simpsons on TV
FRIDAY	see the new film with Nigel

1 have a tennis lesson / Monday?
Is Paul going to have a tennis lesson on Monday?
No, he isn't. He's going to have a piano lesson.

2 revise for a test / Tuesday?
_____
_____

3 do the English project / Wednesday?
_____
_____

4 watch *Friends* on TV / Thursday?
_____
_____

5 see the new film with Nigel / Friday?
_____
_____

Writing

6 ■■■ **Write sentences.**

What are you and your friends going to do?
1 This weekend, I _____ .
2 My sister / brother / friend _____ .
3 We _____ .
4 My parents _____ .

What are you not going to do?
5 I _____ .
6 My sister / brother / friend _____ .
7 We _____ .
8 My parents _____ .

6B At the movies

Adverbs

1 * Write the adverbs.

adjective	adverb
bad	*badly*
beautiful	
careful	
easy	
fast	
good	
happy	
hard	
heavy	
horrible	
loud	
quick	
quiet	
slow	
sudden	

2 ** Complete the sentences with the adverbs in exercise 1.

1 She is acting b*adly*____.

2 They are moving s________.

3 S________, a monster jumped out in front of them.

4 He is walking c________.

5 They are talking l________.

6 He is working h________.

7 They are watching q________.

8 They are laughing h________.

9 She is acting w________.

10 He is driving f________.

3 ★★ Complete the sentences with adjectives or adverbs.

1 Jack's a good swimmer.
  Jack can swim _____*well*_____.

2 Sebastian's a bad dancer.
  Sebastian dances _____.

3 Kim's very careful.
  Kim does everything _____.

4 John can run fast.
  John is a _____ runner.

5 There was a sudden noise.
  _____, there was a noise.

6 I don't play music very loudly.
  I don't like _____ music.

4 ★★ 🎧 1.29 Listen to a teacher and match the children to how they wrote the test.

| slowly badly quickly very well ~~carefully~~ |

1 Uma   _____*carefully*_____
2 Sara   _____
3 Daniel   _____
4 Jane   _____
5 Harry   _____

5 ★★ Choose the correct words to complete the sentences.

1 Come and swim! The water is (warm) / warmly.

2 Please be **quiet** / **quietly**. The children are writing a test.

3 I heard a **loud** / **loudly** noise.

4 Oh dear. I did very **bad** / **badly** in my test.

5 I can dance but not very **good** / **well**.

6 She plays the piano **beautifully** / **beautiful**.

7 The crocodile opens its mouth **slow** / **slowly** and then shuts it again very **quick** / **quickly**.

8 This film is so **horrible** / **horribly**!

9 My bag is very **heavy** / **heavily**.

10 This exercise is **easy** / **easily**.

Writing

6 ★★★ Answer the questions.

1 What do you do slowly?

I write slowly.

I read slowly.

2 What do you do carefully?

_____

3 How well can you play football?

_____

4 Do you talk quietly or loudly with your friends?

_____

5 What do you do badly?

_____

6 What do you do well?

_____

Types of films

1 * Label the pictures with types of films.

1 _a thriller_

2 _____

3 _____

4 _____

5 _____

6 _____

7 _____

8 _____

2 ** Complete the sentences with types of films.

1 The new Mr Bean film is the funniest _comedy_ film in the world!

2 I was so scared. I really don't like h_____ films.

3 I like films with a happy ending, especially r_____ c_____, where there is a wedding at the end.

4 My favourite films are t_____. They are so exciting and full of action.

5 I don't like m_____ because I hate it when people start singing in the middle of a film.

6 I love all of the Star Wars films because I like s_____ f_____.

7 The Harry Potter films are my favourite f_____ films.

8 _Rio_ is a great c_____ about a parrot but _Madagascar 3_ is better!

3 *** Answer the questions in full.

1 What is your favourite film?
   My favourite film is ... _____

2 What kind of films do you like best?
   _____
   _____

3 What kind of films don't you like?
   _____
   _____

4 Who is your favourite actor?
   _____
   _____

5 How often do you watch films at the cinema?
   _____

6 How often do you watch films on TV?
   _____
   _____

have to

4 ✱✱ **Look at the list. What do Howard and Meg have to do this week?**

	Howard	Meg
take the dog for a walk	✓	✗
go to the dentist	✗	✓
practise the piano	✓	✓
revise for a test	✗	✗
help with the housework	✓	✓
cook dinner	✗	✓
buy a present	✓	✗

1 Howard _has to take the dog_ for a walk.
2 Meg _doesn't have to take the dog_ for a walk.
3 Meg _____ to the dentist.
4 Howard and Meg _____ the piano.
5 They _____ for a test.
6 They _____ with the housework.
7 Meg _____ dinner.
8 She _____ a present.

5 ✱✱ 🎧 1.30 **Listen to Simon talking about his weekend. Tick (✓) the things he has to do and cross (✗) the things he doesn't have to do.**

1	Get up early	✓
2	Revise for a test	
3	Go to sports training	
4	Tidy his room	
5	Go shopping	
6	Make his lunch	
7	Take the dog for a walk	

Writing

6 ✱✱✱ **Write the questions and answers about yourself using _have to_.**

1 you / do homework at the weekend?
   Do you have to do homework at the weekend?
   Yes, I do. I don't have to do homework on
   Saturdays but I have to do homework on
   Sundays.

2 you / go shopping with your parents?
   _____
   _____

3 you and your classmates / stand up when a teacher comes into the classroom?
   _____
   _____

4 What jobs / you / do in the house?
   _____
   _____

5 How often / you / tidy your room?
   _____
   _____

6 What time / you / get up / on school days?
   _____
   _____

6D The lost penguin

Making suggestions

1 ✱▬▬ **Complete the dialogue with the sentences (a–f).**

a Let's come again next weekend.

~~b Let's go to the zoo to see the penguins.~~

c Let's look on the signpost.

d They're £2 each.

e Why don't we come back later when it's quieter?

f Why don't we walk?

Tom	I'm bored. What shall we do?
Matt	¹ _Let's go to the zoo to see the penguins._
Tom	Good idea!
Tom	I hate waiting for the bus.
Matt	² _____
Tom	OK.
Matt	Let's buy a map of the zoo.
Tom	³ _____
Matt	Oh, OK, let's not buy one!
Tom	Where are the penguins?
Matt	I don't know.
Tom	⁴ _____
Matt	Wow, there are lots of people here.
Tom	⁵ _____
Matt	No, I think they are feeding the penguins now. It'll be fun.
Tom	I'm glad we came. This is great.
Matt	⁶ _____
Tom	Good idea.

2 ✱▬▬ **Match the words in A to the words in B to make phrases.**

A	B
go	shopping
play	a pizza
watch	a film
have	computer games
go	a CD
pack	the match on TV
watch	on the Internet
listen to	our suitcases

3 ✱✱▬ **Complete the sentences with the phrases in exercise 2.**

1 • Why _don't we have a pizza_?

○ That's a good idea. I'm going to have ham and mushrooms on mine.

2 • Let's _____.

○ OK. We can look for information about the theatre.

3 • Shall _____?

○ Yes, that's a good idea. I must buy a present for my mum.

4 • Let's _____.

○ OK. Who is playing?

5 • Why _____
_____?

○ OK. But be careful, I'm really good. I always win every game!

6 • Shall _____?

○ OK. Shall I meet you in front of the cinema?

7 • Why _____
_____?

○ OK, but not loudly because my mum hates loud music.

8 • Shall _____ today?

○ Good idea. We have to be at the airport at eight o'clock in the morning.

4 ★★ **Complete the sentences so they all have the same meaning.**

1 a Let's watch something else.
  b Shall _we watch_ something else?
  c Why _don't we watch_ something else?

2 a Shall we go swimming?
  b Let's _____ swimming.
  c Why _____ swimming?

3 a Let's go to the cinema tonight.
  b Why _____ to the cinema tonight?
  c Shall _____ to the cinema tonight?

4 a Why don't we make a cake?
  b Shall _____ a cake?
  c Let's _____ a cake.

5 a Let's have a cola.
  b Why _____ a cola?
  c Shall _____ a cola?

5 ★★★ (1.31) **Listen and complete the notes.**

1
Friday
Going to: _the cinema_
Meeting at (place):
Meeting at (time):

2
Saturday
Going to:
Meeting at (place):
Meeting at (time):

3
Sunday
Going to:
Meeting at (place):
Meeting at (time):

4
Wednesday
Going to:
Meeting at (place):
Meeting at (time):

5
Thursday
Going to:
Meeting at (place):
Meeting at (time):

Progress check

1 Circle the correct words.

1 'Why are you laughing?' 'I'm watching **the news** / ~~a comedy show~~ / **a documentary**.'

2 My uncle works for a TV company. He makes **documentaries / films / police dramas** about animals.

3 *River City* is one of the most popular **films / reality shows / soap operas** in Scotland. Every week, people watch to see what happens to their favourite characters in the story.

4 It's important to know about things in the world. That's why I always watch **comedy shows / reality shows / the news**.

5 I love **police dramas / quiz shows / soap operas**, because I often answer all the questions!

6 When they make a character in **the news / a soap opera / a cartoon**, they have to draw lots of pictures and then use a computer to make them 'move'.

2 Write the types of films.

1 It's very funny. Owen Wilson is the main actor and he is the funniest man in the world!

   comedy

2 Lots of famous people do the voices of the characters. Ben Stiller does the voice of Alex the lion.

   _____

3 It's about a magic land full of wizards and talking animals.

   _____

4 The singing is great and the dancing and costumes, too.

   _____

5 It's really scary. Sometimes you have to close your eyes when the monster comes out of the dark night.

   _____

6 It's about a man who travels in time and space.

   _____

3 Complete the dialogue with *going to* and the verbs in brackets.

- Are you [1] _going to study_ (study) tonight?
- No, I'm too tired.
  I [2] _____ (watch) a DVD.
- Why don't you come to the sports centre with me? I [3] _____ (play) basketball.
- Who [4] _____ (play) with?
- Tom, Anna and some other friends.
  We [5] _____ (meet) at seven o'clock.
- [6] _____ (you / take) the bus?
- No, I [7] _____ (go) by bike. It isn't far.
- Wow. Cycling and basketball in one evening!
- So, [8] _____ (you / come) with us?
- I don't know. My parents [9] _____ (be) home late and I have to look after my little sister. We [10] _____ (watch) *Diary of a Wimpy Kid*. She loves that film.
- OK. Well, enjoy the film.
- Thanks.

4 🎧 1.32 Listen to an interview with an actor and circle the correct words.

The actor:
1 works ~~hard~~ / **slowly**.
2 learns his lines **easily / carefully**.
3 is going to **work on television / make a film**.
4 isn't going to **work in America / get married**.
5 sings **badly / well**.

The interviewer says:
6 Shall we **sing a song / watch a film**?
7 Let's talk about your **new film / family**.
8 Why don't you **go to Hollywood / make a CD**?

5 **Make sentences using *have to* / *don't have to*.**

1   Ted is a teacher.

(work on Saturdays / prepare lessons)

He doesn't have to work on Saturdays.

He has to prepare lessons.

2   Miranda is on a school trip.

(go to school / get up early)

_____

_____

3   They are school children.

(do homework / go to school on Sundays)

_____

_____

4   Annie is a waitress.

(cook food / bring food to customers)

_____

_____

5   Seth works in a zoo on Saturdays.

(feed the animals / buy a ticket for the zoo)

_____

_____

I can ...

Write the answers and tick (✓) the correct box.

1   On Monday [1]*I'm going to*
    watch TV. (watch TV)
    Next week my parents
    [2]_____. (buy an MP3 player)

I can talk about plans.

☐ Yes   ☐ I need more practice

2   I like [1]_____, but
    I don't like [2]_____
    very much.

I can say what TV programmes / films I like watching.

☐ Yes   ☐ I need more practice

3   go / Let's / to / cinema / the
    • [1] *Let's go to the cinema*!
    idea / That's / good / a
    ○ [2]_____.
    we / Why / meet / don't / the bus stop / at
    • [3]_____?
    we / meet / Shall / two o'clock / at
    ○ [4]_____?
    OK / you / See / there
    • [5]_____.

I can make suggestions.

☐ Yes   ☐ I need more practice

Revision

1 🔊 1.33 Listen to the interview and answer the questions.

1 Has he got any brothers or sisters?
   Yes, he has. He's got one brother.

2 What subjects does Josh like?
   _____

3 What sports does Josh do?
   _____

4 When does he do sport?
   _____

5 What does he usually do at the weekend?
   _____

6 Does he like playing computer games?
   _____

7 What jobs does he have to do in the house?
   _____

2 Write about Tony and Stephanie. Use a verb and the correct form of *have to*.

Tony	✓	✓	✗	✗
Stephanie	✗	✓	✓	✗

1 Tony _has to feed_ the dog.
2 Stephanie _____ the dog.
3 Tony and Stephanie _____ the shopping.
4 Stephanie _____ the recycling.
5 Tony _____ the recycling.
6 Tony and Stephanie _____ the floor.

3 Write the correct form of the verbs in brackets.

1 Every Tuesday, after school I _have_ (have) a music lesson. But today I _____ (go) to the dentist, so I _____ (not have) a music lesson.

2 Karl usually _____ (watch) TV in the evenings, but tonight he _____ (play) football for the school team.

3 I always _____ (read) a lot when I go on holiday. At the moment, I _____ (read) a book by Phillip Pullman.

4 Angela _____ (not / usually / go) to bed late. But tonight she _____ (go) to bed later, because she has to finish her homework.

4 What did Sara buy? Write questions and answers with *some* or *any*.

Shopping list
oil ✓	rice ✓
tomatoes ✗	beans ✓
water ✗	meat ✗

1 _Did she buy any oil?_
   Yes, she bought some oil.

2 _____
   _____

3 _____
   _____

4 _____
   _____

5 _____
   _____

6 _____
   _____

5 Complete the sentences with one word in each gap.

1   _Are_   there any grapes?
2   _____ there any meat?
3   There _____ some cheese.
4   There _____ some apples.
5   How _____ eggs are there?
6   How _____ milk is there?
7   I went to the shop and bought a _____ of bread.
8   Do you have one _____ of toast for breakfast or two?

6 What happened to Andy on holiday? Complete the sentences with the words in the box in the past simple tense.

eat	close	leave	lose	start	take
be	watch	drive	get	have	

Hi Craig,

The first day of our holiday [1]_____was_____ terrible! First, we [2]_____ to the wrong hotel. We finally [3]_____ to our hotel at ten o'clock. But they [4]_____ the restaurant at half past nine! I was lucky – I [5]_____ an apple in my bag.

The next morning, we [6]_____ a taxi to the beach. We drove for a long time. At the beach, it [7]_____ raining. We [8]_____ in a café and [9]_____ the rain. Then we went back to the hotel by bus. But my mother [10]_____ her bag on the bus! So we [11]_____ all our money. It was a bad day!

Bye,
Andy

7 Complete the text with the correct form of the adjectives in brackets.

I think *Looney Tunes* is funny, but *Tom and Jerry* is much [1]_____funnier_____ (funny). But the [2]_____ (good) cartoon of all is *The Simpsons*. My favourite character is Homer. He's [3]_____ (old) and [4]_____ (fat) than Marge, his wife. She's much [5]_____ (nice) than Homer. Maggie, the baby, is [6]_____ (young) of the three children. The [7]_____ (old) child is Bart. I think he's [8]_____ (bad) at schoolwork in his class!

8 Look at Valerie's diary. Write what she is going to do or not going to do next week.

Monday	play ~~tennis~~ badminton
Tuesday	finish my homework
Wednesday	~~go to the cinema with Melanie~~ watch a DVD with Melanie
Thursday	cook dinner for ~~Tom~~ Dan
Friday	buy tickets for the concert

1   On Monday, she _isn't going to play_ tennis. She _____ badminton.
2   On Tuesday, she _____ her homework.
3   On Wednesday, Valerie and Melanie _____ to the cinema. They _____ a DVD.
4   On Thursday, Valerie _____ dinner for Tom. She _____ dinner for Dan.
5   On Friday, she _____ tickets for the concert.

Grammar summary

1 My life

1.1 Present simple: affirmative

I We You They	have buy	a holiday in May. presents for the children.
He She It	visits lives	Scotland in November. on a farm.

a To make the present simple, we use the infinitive. For *he*, *she* and *it*, we add *-s*.

b We use the present simple to talk about things that happen repeatedly. We also use the present simple to talk about facts that are generally true.

c Note these spelling rules:

1 With verbs ending in *-o*, add *-es*.
   She **goes** *to the sports centre every day.*

2 With verbs ending in *-ch*, *-sh*, *-s*, *-x* or *-z*, add *-es*.

We pronounce the *-es* as /ɪz/.
She **watches** *TV.*

1.2 Present simple: negative

To make the negative of the present simple we use *don't / doesn't* and the infinitive.

I **don't live** *in Britain.*   *She* **doesn't like** *school.*

1.3 Present simple: questions

To make questions in the present simple, we use *do / does* and the infinitive.

Do *you* **go** *to bed late on Saturday?*

For *Wh-* questions we add the question word at the beginning.

Where *do you live?* **When** *does she do her homework?*

1.4 Present simple: short answers

To make short answers, we do not repeat the main verb. We use only *do / does* in the affirmative and *don't / doesn't* in the negative.

Do you play the violin?   *Yes, I* **do**. (NOT *Yes, I play.*)

Does he live on a farm?   *No, he* **doesn't**. (NOT *No, he doesn't live.*)

1.5 Ordinal numbers

1st	first	20th	twentieth
2nd	second	30th	thirtieth
3rd	third	40th	fortieth
4th	fourth	50th	fiftieth
5th	fifth	60th	sixtieth
6th	sixth	70th	seventieth
7th	seventh	80th	eightieth
8th	eighth	90th	ninetieth
9th	ninth	100th	hundredth
10th	tenth		

a We use ordinal numbers for dates.

My birthday is the **twenty-seventh** *of June.*

b We also use them to describe the order of a noun.

This is my **fourth** *visit to England.*
We live on the **second** *floor.*

Translate
New Year's Day is the first of January.
November is the eleventh month of the year.

1.6 Adverbs of frequency

always usually / normally often sometimes never

a We use adverbs of frequency to tell us how often something happens. We ask questions about frequency with *How often ...?*

How often *do you go to the cinema?*

b We usually put adverbs of frequency before a verb.

I **usually** *watch TV in the evening.*

c When there is an auxiliary verb (e.g. *do*, *don't*), we put adverbs of frequency after the auxiliary and before the main verb.

I don't **often** *go to the cinema.*
What do you **usually** *watch on TV?*

d We usually put adverbs of frequency after the verb *be*.

It's **always** *cold in winter.*

Translate
I usually watch TV before I do my homework.
We don't often go to football matches.
How often do you go to pop concerts?
I'm usually not at home on Wednesdays.

2 Animals

2.1 Present continuous: affirmative

I	am 'm	
We You They	are 're	sleeping. reading a magazine. wearing jeans.
He She It	is 's	

We use the present continuous to talk about something that is happening at the moment we speak.

Note these spelling rules:

1 with most verbs, add -ing.
   go – going
2 with verbs ending in -e, drop the -e and add -ing.
   take – taking
3 with verbs ending in a short vowel and one consonant, double the consonant.
   sit – sitting

2.2 Present continuous: negative

To make the negative we add *not* after the verb *be*.

You are not going shopping.
(long form)

They aren't taking the bus.
(short form)

2.3 Present continuous: questions

a To make questions in the present continuous we put *Am*, *Is* or *Are* in front of the subject.

   He is taking a photo. Is he taking a photo?

b For *Wh-* questions we add the question word at the beginning.

   When are you going shopping?
   Why is he taking a photo?
   What are they doing?

2.4 Present continuous: short answers

To make short answers, we use only the verb *be*, NOT the -ing form. The verb *be* is in the full form, not the short form.

Is she wearing her school uniform?
Yes, she is. (NOT *Yes, she is wearing* or *Yes, she's*)

2.5 Present simple and continuous

I go to school every day.
I am going to school now.
Tony gets up at eight o'clock every day.
It is eight o'clock now. Tony is getting up.

Translate
She waits for the bus every day.
She is waiting for the bus at the moment.

2.6 *must*

I You He She It We They	must	go home now.

We use *must* when it is necessary to do something.
We don't have an -s in the *he / she / it* form of *must*.
Peter must do his homework.

Translate
You must clean your room.
My sister must buy some new clothes.

2.7 Subject and object pronouns

Subject	Object
I	me
you	you
he	him
she	her
it	it
we	us
they	them

subject pronoun		object pronoun
We He	love doesn't love	him. us.

Translate
They see her on Saturdays.
She loves him.

Grammar summary

3 Holidays

3.1 Past simple of *be*: affirmative

I He She It	was	on holiday at school at the cinema ill	last week. yesterday. on Monday.
We You They	were	in London out	

We use the past simple of *be* to talk about a definite time in the past.

Translate
I was at home yesterday.
She was on holiday in England last year.
They were at the cinema on Thursday.

3.2 Past simple of *be*: affirmative

I He She It	was not wasn't	on holiday at school at the cinema ill	last week. yesterday. on Monday.
We You They	were not weren't	in London out	

To make the negative we put *not* after the verb. To make the short form, we use *wasn't / weren't*.

3.3 Past simple of *be*: questions

Was	I he she it	here at five o'clock last week? at home yesterday evening? at the cinema on Friday? on TV yesterday?
Were	we you they	in England two years ago? at home yesterday? ill last week?
Why **were** you at home yesterday?		

a To make questions, we put the verb in front of the subject.

*He was at home yesterday. **Was** he at home yesterday?*

b For *Wh-* questions we add the question word at the beginning.

3.4 Past simple of *be*: short answers

Yes,	I he she it	was.	No,	I he she it	wasn't.
	we you they	were.		we you they	weren't.

Translate
Were you at the cinema yesterday? Yes, I was.
Was he at school last week? No, he wasn't.

3.5 Past simple affirmative: regular verbs

I stayed in bed for three days.
He watched TV all day.
It arrived four days ago.
We needed help last week.
They visited us after school.

a We use the past simple for actions and states which happened at a particular time and are now complete.

We often use it with time expressions, such as *yesterday*, *ago*, *on* (+ day), *in* (+ month / year), and *at* (+ time).

b To make the past simple tense we add *-ed* to the infinitive.

c Note these spelling rules:

1 With verbs ending in *-e*, add *-d*.
We closed our books.

2 With verbs with a short vowel and one consonant at the end, double the consonant and add *-ed*.
They stopped the car. They robbed the bank.
They travelled to Spain.

3 With verbs ending in *-y*, remove the *-y* and add *-ied*.
He studied in London. I carried the bag.

4 Note this pronunciation rule:
When the stem of the verb ends in *-d* or *-t*, the *-ed* ending is pronounced /ɪd/.

She needed an operation. I wanted a book.

3.6 Past simple: negative

I He She It We You They	did not didn't	have lunch yesterday.

To make the negative of the past simple of regular and irregular verbs we use *did not / didn't* and the infinitive. *He went to school. He **didn't go** to school.*

Translate
Did you see your teacher on holiday? No, I didn't.
He didn't write the letter yesterday.

3.7 Past simple affirmative: irregular verbs

I **had** a headache.	It **bit** me.
You **wrote** a letter.	We **got** some medicine.
He **went** to London.	They **drove** home.
She **took** my temperature.	

A lot of verbs are irregular. There is no rule to make these verbs. You need to learn the form for each verb. See page 79 for a list of some irregular verbs.

3.8 Past simple: *Yes / No* questions

Did	I hurt him? he drop the camera? she cut her finger? it ring? we play rugby? you break your leg? they have a headache?

Did is the past of *do*. To make questions in past simple, we use *Did* and the infinitive. We put *Did* in front of the subject.

*She went to London. **Did** she **go** to London?*

3.9 Past simple: short answers

Yes,	I he she it we you they	did.	No,	I he she it we you they	didn't.

To make short answers, we use only *did / didn't* – NOT the infinitive.

Did he play football yesterday?
Yes, he did. (NOT *Yes, he played.*)
Did they go to Paris?
No, they didn't. (NOT *No, they didn't go.*)

3.10 Past simple: *Wh-* questions

a For *Wh-* questions we add the question word at the beginning.

***When** did you go to England?*
***Why** did you come home?*

b When the question word is the subject, we use the full verb.

***Who bought** a new car?*
***What happened** to Mandy?*

Translate
Did you go to London last year?
Did they play tennis yesterday?
When did she go to Paris?

4 Food

4.1 Countable and uncountable nouns

We need some tomatoes. How many do we need?	We need some bread. How much do we need?

a Some nouns are countable. These nouns can be singular or plural.

an apple	*six apples*
an onion	*lots of onions*
a sausage	*100 g of sausages*

b Some nouns are uncountable. These have no singular or plural form.

some milk   *a lot of rice*   *a little butter*

4.2 *a / an*

a potato	an apple
a hamburger	an egg

a *A / an* are indefinite articles. When the following noun begins with a consonant, we use *a*. When the following noun begins with a vowel (or vowel sound), we use *an*.

b We don't use *a / an* with plurals or uncountable nouns. (see 4.3)

Translate

You need a frying pan.
You need an egg.
I like apples.
There's sugar in this tea.

4.3 some and any

I've got **some** books.
I haven't got **any** food.
Have you got **any** money?

a   We use *some* and *any* with countable nouns in the plural and with uncountable nouns.

   some books
   some money

b   We use *some* when the sentence is positive.

   We use *any* when the sentence is negative or a question.
   Is there **any** milk?
   There isn't **any** time.

4.4 How much? / How many?

We use *How many* to ask about the quantity of countable nouns.
How many oranges have you got?
We use *How much* to ask about the quantity of uncountable nouns.
How much cheese do you want?

Translate

How much milk do we need?
How many eggs do we need?

4.5 Definite and indefinite articles

You need **some** oil and **a** frying pan.
Put **the** oil in **the** frying pan.

a   We use *a / an* when we mention a singular, countable noun for the first time.

b   We use *the* when we know or can see which thing or person we are talking about or when we mention it for a second time.

c   We use the same form of *the* for singular and plural countable nouns and for uncountable nouns.

   the apple   **the** onions   **the** water

Translate

Slice the onions.
Put the flour in the bowl.
I've got a sandwich for lunch.

4.6 Quantity: a little and a few

a little a few	salt butter carrots

We use *a little* and *a few* to talk about small quantities. We use *a little* with uncountable nouns and *a few* with plural countable nouns.

5 The world

5.1 How questions

How	long high deep	is this street? is this building? is this ocean?	It's 400 metres **long**. It's 20 metres **high**. It's 2 kilometres **deep**.

We use *How* with an adjective to ask about the measurements of something. We can use the same adjective in the answer.
How long is this river? It's 500 kilometres **long**.

Translate

How wide is the Amazon?
How deep is the Atlantic Ocean?

5.2 Comparatives

We use the comparative when we compare two things or people. After a comparative we use *than*.
Canada is **larger than** England.

a   To form the comparative of most short adjectives (adjectives with one syllable), we usually add *-er*.

   small – small**er**   warm – warm**er**

b   With adjectives which end in *-e*, just add *-r*.

   large – larg**er**   nice – nic**er**

c   With adjectives which end in one consonant after a short vowel, double the consonant and add *-er*.

   hot – hot**ter**   big – big**ger**

d   With adjectives which end in *-y*, change the *-y* to *-i* and add *-er*.

   dirty – dirt**ier**   easy – eas**ier**

e   With adjectives with two or more syllables (except when the second syllable ends in *-y*), put *more* before the adjective.

   interesting – **more** interesting

f Some adjectives are irregular.

far – further

Translate
Scotland is smaller than England.
I am taller than my best friend.

5.3 Superlatives

Adjective	Comparative	Superlative
small	smaller	the smallest
nice	nicer	the nicest
wet	wetter	the wettest
heavy	heavier	the heaviest
modern	more modern	the most modern
far	further	the furthest

We use the superlative when we compare three or more things or people. We use *the* before the superlative.

*Mount Everest is **the highest** mountain in the world.*

a To form the superlative of adjectives we use *the* and *-est*.

b With adjectives with two or more syllables (except when the second syllable ends in *-y*), put *most* before the adjective.

c Spelling changes also apply to the superlative form.

Adjective	Comparative	Superlative
big	bigger	the biggest
hot	hotter	the hottest
easy	easier	the easiest

Translate
I'm the oldest student in my class.
What is the furthest planet from Earth?

5.4 Comparatives and superlatives: *good* and *bad*

Adjective	Comparative	Superlative
good	better	the best
bad	worse	the worst

The comparative and superlative forms of *good* and *bad* are irregular.

Translate
I think football is better than basketball.
The worst subject is Maths.
Andy is the best student in our class.

5.5 Comparatives and superlatives with *more* and *the most*

Adjective	Comparative	Superlative
gorgeous	more gorgeous	the most gorgeous
expensive	more expensive	the most expensive
intelligent	more intelligent	the most intelligent

We make the comparatives of adjectives with more than one syllable with *more*. We make the superlative with *the most*, except where the second syllable is *-y*.

useful   *more useful*   ***the most** useful*
BUT   *happy*   *happier*   *the happiest*

Translate
Geography is more difficult than Maths.
He bought the most beautiful card in the shop.
Who is the most intelligent person in the class?

5.6 *as … as*

as heavy as lead   as white as snow

We use *as … as* to say two things or people are the same.

Sometimes we use *as … as* in fixed phrases.
***as** warm **as** toast*   ***as** dry **as** a bone*

Translate
My sister is as tall as me.
That building is as high as a mountain.

6 Entertainment

6.1 *going to*: affirmative

I	am 'm		
He She It	is 's	going to	visit Grandma next week. have pizza for lunch. buy a new CD tomorrow.
We You They	are 're		

To make *going to* we use *be* and *going to* and the infinitive. We can use *going to* to talk about what we have decided to do in the future.

Translate
I'm going to watch TV this evening.
They're going to have lunch in a restaurant tomorrow.

Grammar summary

6.2 *going to*: negative

I	am not 'm not		
He She It	is not isn't	going to	phone Tim. play in the garden. play computer games.
We You They	are not aren't		

To make the negative form of *going to*, we use the correct form of the negative of *be*.

Translate

He isn't going to get up early tomorrow.
We aren't going to eat at home today.

6.3 *going to*: questions

Am	I		
Is	he she it	going to	see you this evening? do today's homework? rain this afternoon? have a party?
Are	we you they		
What is she **going to** sing?			

a To make questions with *going to*, we put the verb *be* in front of the subject.

   ***Are** they **going to** play football?*

b For *Wh-* questions we add the question word at the beginning.

   ***What** are you going to do this weekend?*

Translate

Are you going to have a pizza?
What are you going to do on your birthday?

6.4 *going to*: short answers

	I	am.		I'm	not.
Yes,	we you they	are.	No,	we you they	aren't.
	he she it	is.		he she it	isn't.

To make short answers, we use the verb *be*, NOT *going to*.

Translate

Is she going to play tennis tomorrow? Yes, she is.
Are they going to phone you this evening? No, they aren't.

6.5 Adjectives and adverbs

Adjective	Adverb
The car is **slow**.	It moves **slowly**.
He was **quiet**.	He spoke **quietly**.
She's **happy**.	She's singing **happily**.

a Adjectives describe nouns – they say what something is like.

   *He was a **horrible man**.*

b Adverbs describe verbs – they say how you do something.

   *She opened her eyes **quickly**.*

c We make the adverb by adding *-ly* to the adjective.

   careful – carefully   loud – loudly

d With adjectives that end in *-y*, change the *-y* to *-i* in the adverb.

   easy – easily   happy – happily

e These adverbs are irregular.

   fast – fast   good – well   hard – hard

*This is a **fast** car. The car travels **fast**.*
*He is a **good** driver. He drives **well**.*
*She is a **hard** worker. She works very **hard**.*

Translate

She's careful. She does her homework very carefully.
It's a good robot. It works very well.

6.6 *have to*: affirmative

I We You They	have to	get up early. be very fit. stay outdoors.
He She It	has to	

To show when something is necessary, we use *have / has to* and the infinitive.

Translate

You have to wait.
He has to wear a uniform at school.

6.7 *have to*: negative

I We You They	do not don't	have to	get up early. be very fit. stay outdoors.
He She It	does not doesn't		

a We use *don't have to / doesn't have to* when something is not necessary.

b To make the negative, we add *don't / doesn't* before *have to*.

*I **have to get up** early.*   *I **don't have to get up** early.*

*She **has to work**.*   *She **doesn't have to work**.*

Translate
We don't have to go to school on Saturdays.
He doesn't have to get up early.

6.8 *have to*: questions

Do	I we you they	have to	wear a uniform? travel a lot? do a lot of homework? sleep outdoors?
Does	he she it		
When do they **have to** go to bed?			

a To make questions with *have to*, we use *Do / Does*, *have to* and the infinitive.

b For *Wh* questions we add the question word at the beginning.

Translate
Do you have to wear a uniform?
Does she have to get up early?

6.9 *have to*: short answers

Yes,	I we you they	do.	No,	I we you they	don't.
	he she it	does.		he she it	doesn't.

To make short answers, we do not repeat *have to* or the main verb. We use only *do / does* in the affirmative and *don't / doesn't* in the negative.

Do you have to travel a lot?   *Yes, I **do**.*
Does she have to work outdoors?   *Yes, she **does**.*

Translate
Do they have to wear a uniform? Yes, they do.
Does she have to do her homework? No, she doesn't.

6.10 Making suggestions

a We make suggestions with:
1 *Why don't we* and the infinitive.
   ***Why don't we play** tennis?*
2 *Let's* and the infinitive.
   ***Let's watch** TV.*
3 *Shall we* and the infinitive.
   ***Shall we meet** outside the sports centre?*

b We also use *shall* with question words to ask for a suggestion.
   ***Where shall** we meet?*

c If you agree with a suggestion, you can say:
OK, that's a good idea or *All right*.
Shall we go shopping? **All right**.
Why don't we go to the cinema? **That's a good idea**.

Translate
Let's go swimming.
Why don't we have a pizza?
When shall we meet?

Wordlist

Introduction

Introductions
best friend /ˌbest 'frend/
dark hair /ˈdɑːk ˌheə(r)/
garden /ˈɡɑːdn/
Her / His / My name's ... /ˈhɜː, ˈhɪz, ˈmaɪ ˌneɪmz/
He's / She's ... /hiːz, ʃiːz/
Hi. /haɪ/
I'm ... /aɪm/
live /lɪv/
neighbour /ˈneɪbə(r)/
next door /ˌnekst ˈdɔː(r)/
over there /ˌəʊvə ˈðeə(r)/
people /ˈpiːpl/
short hair /ˈʃɔːt ˌheə(r)/
the boy / girl with ... /ðə ˈbɔɪ, ˈɡɜːl wɪð/
Their names are ... /ˈðeə ˌneɪmz ˌɑː(r), ə(r)/
These are ... /ˈðiːz ˌɑː(r), ə(r)/
This is / That's ... /ˈðɪs ˌɪz, ˈðæts/
Welcome to ... /ˈwelkəm tə/
What's her / his / your name? /ˌwɒts ˈhɜː, ˈhɪz, jɔː ˌneɪm/
Who are / Who's ...? /ˈhuː ˌɑː(r), ə(r), huːz/

At the sports centre
activity /æk'tɪvəti/
address /əˈdres/
age /eɪdʒ/
child (children) /tʃaɪld (ˈtʃɪldrən)/
club /klʌb/
email address /ˈiːmeɪl əˌdres/
How old is ...? /ˈhaʊ ˌəʊld ˌɪz/
include /ɪnˈkluːd/
interested (in) /ˈɪntrəstɪd (ˌɪn)/
join /dʒɔɪn/
membership card /ˈmembəʃɪp ˌkɑːd/
open /ˈəʊpən/
postcode /ˈpəʊstkəʊd/
receptionist /rɪˈsepʃənɪst/
sport /spɔːt/
sports centre /ˈspɔːts ˌsentə(r)/
telephone number /ˈtelɪfəʊn ˌnʌmbə(r)/
Where does she live? /ˌweə dəz ˈʃiː ˈlɪv/

Sports and activities
badminton /ˈbædmɪntən/
basketball /ˈbɑːskɪtbɔːl/
fitness class /ˈfɪtnəs ˌklɑːs/
football /ˈfʊtbɔːl/
karate /kəˈrɑːti/
swimming /ˈswɪmɪŋ/
table tennis /ˈteɪbl ˌtenɪs/
tennis /ˈtenɪs/
volleyball /ˈvɒlibɔːl/
weight training /ˈweɪt ˌtreɪnɪŋ/
yoga /ˈjəʊɡə/

What can you do?
bike /baɪk/
both /bəʊθ/
Can you ...? /ˈkæn, kən ˌjuː/
count from ... to ... /ˌkaʊnt frəm ˈ... tə/
divide ... by ... /dɪˌvaɪd ˈ... ˌbaɪ/
English /ˈɪŋɡlɪʃ/
French /frentʃ/
ice hockey /ˈaɪs ˌhɒki/
metre /ˈmiːtə(r)/
ride /raɪd/
speak /spiːk/
spell /spel/
swim /swɪm/
throw /θrəʊ/
write /raɪt/
Yes, I can. / No, I can't. /ˌjes ˌaɪ ˈkæn, ˌnəʊ ˌaɪ ˈkɑːnt/

In the street
bag /bæɡ/
box /bɒks/
carry /ˈkæri/
holiday /ˈhɒlədeɪ/
How many ... are there? /ˌhaʊ ˌmeni ˈ... ˌɑː ˌðeə/
memory /ˈmeməri/
poster /ˈpəʊstə(r)/
tennis racquet /ˈtenɪs ˌrækɪt/
wear /weə(r)/
What colour is / are ...? /ˈwɒt ˌkʌlər ˌɪz, ˌɑː(r), ə(r)/
What's this? /ˌwɒts ˈðɪs/
What is / are ... doing? /ˌwɒt ˌɪz, ɑː(r), ə(r) ... ˈduːɪŋ/
Where is / are ...? /ˈweər ˌɪz, ˌɑː(r), ə(r)/

What has he got?
a bit of /ə ˈbɪt əv/
a lot of /ə ˈlɒt əv/
apple /ˈæpl/
back /bæk/
chance /tʃɑːns/
Come on! /ˈkʌm ˌɒn/
dance /dɑːns/
desk /desk/
do /duː/
drink /drɪŋk/
everybody / everyone /ˈevribɒdi, ˈevriwʌn/
exercise book /ˈeksəsaɪz ˌbʊk/
give /ɡɪv/
have got /həv ˈɡɒt/
hips /hɪps/
jump /dʒʌmp/
key /kiː/
know /nəʊ/
learn /lɜːn/
little /ˈlɪtl/
make /meɪk/
mobile (phone) /ˌməʊbaɪl (ˈfəʊn)/
now /naʊ/
orange /ˈɒrɪndʒ/
pen /pen/
photograph (photo) /ˈfəʊtəɡrɑːf (ˈfəʊtəʊ)/
ruler /ˈruːlə(r)/
sandwich /ˈsænwɪtʃ/
song /sɒŋ/
swing /swɪŋ/
thing /θɪŋ/
train /treɪn/
umbrella /ʌmˈbrelə/
up /ʌp/
watch /wɒtʃ/

1 My life

1A My daily life
after /ˈɑːftə(r)/
assembly /əˈsembli/
at the moment /ət ðə ˈməʊmənt/
at the weekend /ət ðə wiːkˈend/
band /bænd/
before /bɪˈfɔː(r)/
block of flats /ˌblɒk əv ˈflæts/
city /ˈsɪti/
correct /kəˈrekt/
cue /kjuː/
daily /ˈdeɪli/
don't / doesn't like /ˌdəʊnt, ˌdʌznt ˈlaɪk/
favourite /ˈfeɪvərɪt/
flat (n) /flæt/
good (at) /ˈɡʊd (ət)/
grow up /ˌɡrəʊ ˈʌp/
happen /ˈhæpən/
high school /ˈhaɪ ˌskuːl/
I'm ... years old. /ˌaɪm ... ˌjɪəz ˈəʊld/
in the evening /ˌɪn ðiː ˈiːvnɪŋ/
leave home /ˌliːv ˈhəʊm/
lesson /ˈlesn/
life /laɪf/

like /laɪk/
morning /ˈmɔːnɪŋ/
near /nɪə(r)/
on the ... floor /ˌɒn ðə ... ˈflɔː(r)/
practise /ˈpræktɪs/
really /ˈriːəli, ˈrɪəli/
registration /ˌredʒɪˈstreɪʃn/
right /raɪt/
school /skuːl/
sixth form college /ˈsɪksθ ˌfɔːm ˌkɒlɪdʒ/
subject /ˈsʌbʒɪkt/
too /tuː/
walk /wɔːk/
wrong /rɒŋ/
yet /jet/

Ordinal numbers
first /fɜːst/
second /ˈsekənd/
third /θɜːd/
fourth /fɔːθ/
fifth /fɪfθ/
sixth /sɪksθ/
seventh /ˈsevnθ/
eighth /eɪtθ/
ninth /naɪnθ/
tenth /tenθ/
eleventh /ɪˈlevnθ/
twelfth /twelfθ/
thirteenth /θɜːˈtiːnθ/
fourteenth /fɔːˈtiːnθ/
twentieth /ˈtwentiəθ/
twenty-first /ˌtwenti ˈfɜːst/
twenty-second /ˌtwenti ˈsekənd/
thirtieth /ˈθɜːtiəθ/

1B Birthdays
a long time /ə ˌlɒŋ ˈtaɪm/
birthday cake /ˈbɜːθdeɪ ˌkeɪk/
birthday card /ˈbɜːθdeɪ ˌkɑːd/
blow out /ˌbləʊ ˈaʊt/
bowling alley /ˈbəʊlɪŋ ˌæli/
buy /baɪ/
candle /ˈkændl/
CD /ˌsiː ˈdiː/
celebrate /ˈselɪbreɪt/
cinema /ˈsɪnəmə/
clean /kliːn/
close to /ˈkləʊs tə/
date /deɪt/
day /deɪ/
decide /dɪˈsaɪd/
each /iːtʃ/
extra /ˈekstrə/
flowers /ˈflaʊəz/
get /ɡet/
go on holiday /ˌɡəʊ ˌɒn ˈhɒlədeɪ/
Happy Birthday! /ˌhæpi ˈbɜːθdeɪ/
have a party /ˌhæv ə ˈpɑːti/
hear /hɪə(r)/
important /ɪmˈpɔːtnt/
in ... days' time /ˌɪn ... ˌdeɪz ˈtaɪm/
list /lɪst/
look at /ˈlʊk ət/
make a wish /ˌmeɪk ə ˈwɪʃ/
maybe /ˈmeɪbi/
money /ˈmʌni/
month /mʌnθ/
name day /ˈneɪm ˌdeɪ/
not ... much /ˈnɒt ... ˌmʌtʃ/
older /ˈəʊldə(r)/
only /ˈəʊnli/
other /ˈʌðə(r)/
own /əʊn/
present (n) /ˈpreznt/
problem /ˈprɒbləm/
same /seɪm/
sing /sɪŋ/
some /sʌm, səm/
someone / somebody /ˈsʌmwʌn, ˈsʌmbədi/
somewhere /ˈsʌmweə(r)/
sweet (n) /swiːt/

take /teɪk/
today /tə'deɪ/
toy /tɔɪ/
What's the date today? /'wɒts ðə ˌdeɪt
   tə̩deɪ/
When is your birthday? /'wen ˌɪz ˌjɔː
   ˌbɜːθdeɪ/

Months of the year
January /'dʒænjuəri/
February /'februəri/
March /mɑːtʃ/
April /'eɪprəl/
May /meɪ/
June /dʒuːn/
July /dʒu'laɪ/
August /'ɔːgəst/
September /sep'tembə(r)/
October /ɒk'təʊbə(r)/
November /nəʊ'vembə(r)/
December /dɪ'sembə(r)/

1C Mickey, Millie and Mut
agree /ə'griː/
all /ɔːl/
answer /'ɑːnsə(r)/
clever /'klevə(r)/
coffee /'kɒfi/
come from /'kʌm frəm/
Good idea. /ˌgʊd aɪ'dɪə/
hate /heɪt/
I'm not sure. /ˌaɪm ˌnɒt 'ʃʊə(r)/
interview /'ɪntəvjuː/
I've got no idea. /ˌaɪv ˌgɒt 'nəʊ aɪˌdɪə/
last /lɑːst/
mean (v) /miːn/
musical instrument /ˌmjuːzɪkl 'ɪnstrəmənt/
oil /ɔɪl/
OK /ˌəʊ 'keɪ/
penguin /'peŋgwɪn/
polar bear /ˌpəʊlə 'beə(r)/
postman /'pəʊstmən/
quiz /kwɪz/
rubber /'rʌbə(r)/
see /siː/
summer /'sʌmə(r)/
think /θɪŋk/
tree /triː/
Well done! /ˌwel 'dʌn/
winter /'wɪntə(r)/

1D At home
brilliant /'brɪliənt/
busy /'bɪzi/
cup /kʌp/
DJ /'diː ˌdʒeɪ/
do wrong /ˌduː 'rɒŋ/
early /'ɜːli/
exam results /ɪg'zæm rɪˌzʌlts/
great /greɪt/
help /help/
How often …? /'haʊ ˌɒfn, ˌɒftən/
job /dʒɒb/
knives and forks /ˌnaɪvz ən 'fɔːks/
late (for) /'leɪt fə(r)/
meal /miːl/
place /pleɪs/
plate /pleɪt/
put /pʊt/
robot /'rəʊbɒt/
text (v) /tekst/
Which …? /wɪtʃ/

Household jobs
cook the dinner /ˌkʊk ðə 'dɪnə(r)/
do the shopping /ˌduː ðə 'ʃɒpɪŋ/
feed the cat /ˌfiːd ðə 'kæt/
load the dishwasher /ˌləʊd ðə 'dɪʃwɒʃə(r)/
make the bed /ˌmeɪk ðə 'bed/
set the table /ˌset ðə 'teɪbl/
take / put out the recycling /ˌteɪk, ˌpʊt
   ˌaʊt ðə riː'saɪklɪŋ/
take the dog for a walk /ˌteɪk ðə ˌdɒg fər
   ə 'wɔːk/
tidy your room /ˌtaɪdi ˌjɔː 'ruːm/
vacuum the floor /ˌvækjuəm ðə 'flɔː(r)/

Adverbs of frequency
always /'ɔːlweɪz/
never /'nevə(r)/
not often /ˌnɒt 'ɒfn, 'ɒftən/
often /'ɒfn, 'ɒftən/
sometimes /'sʌmtaɪmz/
usually / normally /'juːʒuəli, 'nɔːməli/

Culture
also /'ɔːlsəʊ/
autumn /'ɔːtəm/
because /bɪ'kɒz, bɪ'kəz/
beginning /bɪ'gɪnɪŋ/
bun /bʌn/
chocolate egg /ˌtʃɒklət 'eg/
come together /ˌkʌm tə'geðə(r)/
decorate /'dekəreɪt/
decoration /dekə'reɪʃn/
eat /iːt/
festival /'festɪvl/
fireworks /'faɪəwɜːks/
followed by /'fɒləʊd ˌbaɪ/
go shopping /ˌgəʊ 'ʃɒpɪŋ/
half-term holiday /ˌhɑːf ˌtɜːm 'hɒlədeɪ/
hide /haɪd/
How long …? /'haʊ ˌlɒŋ/
hunt /hʌnt/
in the middle of /ˌɪn ðə 'mɪdl əv/
match /mætʃ/
midnight /'mɪdnaɪt/
music /'mjuːzɪk/
next /nekst/
put up /ˌpʊt 'ʌp/
sale /seɪl/
several /'sevrəl/
spring /sprɪŋ/
street party /'striːt ˌpɑːti/
strike midnight /ˌstraɪk 'mɪdnaɪt/
sweet (adj) /swiːt/
switch on /ˌswɪtʃ 'ɒn/
term /tɜːm/
traditional /trə'dɪʃənl/
turkey /'tɜːki/
typical /'tɪpɪkl/
vegetable /'vedʒtəbl/
visit /'vɪzɪt/
Why …? /waɪ/

Holidays and festivals
Boxing Day /'bɒksɪŋ ˌdeɪ/
Christmas /'krɪsməs/
Christmas Day /ˌkrɪsməs 'deɪ/
Christmas Eve /ˌkrɪsməs 'iːv/
Christmas pudding /ˌkrɪsməs 'pʊdɪŋ/
Christmas tree /'krɪsməs ˌtriː/
Easter /'iːstə(r)/
Easter egg /'iːstər ˌeg/
Easter egg hunt /'iːstər ˌeg ˌhʌnt/
Easter Monday /ˌiːstə 'mʌndeɪ/
Easter Sunday /ˌiːstə 'sʌndeɪ/
Good Friday /ˌgʊd 'fraɪdeɪ/
New Year /ˌnjuː 'jɪə(r)/
New Year's Eve /ˌnjuː ˌjɪəz 'iːv/

English Across the Curriculum
about /ə'baʊt/
add /æd/
at night /ət 'naɪt/
calendar /'kælɪndə(r)/
Earth /ɜːθ/
fix /fɪks/
for example /fər ɪg'zɑːmpl/
go round /ˌgəʊ 'raʊnd/
hour /'aʊə(r)/
in fact /ˌɪn 'fækt/
leap year /'liːp ˌjɪə(r)/
minute /'mɪnɪt/
Moon /muːn/
need /niːd/
nobody /'nəʊbədi/
once /wʌns/
period /'pɪəriəd/
sleep /sliːp/
still /stɪl/
Sun /sʌn/

tie your shoelaces /ˌtaɪ ˌjɔː 'ʃuːleɪsɪz/
turn /tɜːn/
until (till) /ən'tɪl (tɪl)/
use (v) /juːz/

Your Project
dislike (v) /dɪs'laɪk/
event /ɪ'vent/
go sledging /ˌgəʊ 'sledʒɪŋ/
illustrate /'ɪləstreɪt/
mind /maɪnd/
plan /plæn/
rest /rest/
scrapbook /'skræpbʊk/
snow /snəʊ/
stay /steɪ/
think about /'θɪŋk əˌbaʊt/
title /'taɪtl/
trumpet /'trʌmpɪt/

2 Animals

2A Our school trip
coach /kəʊtʃ/
farm /fɑːm/
guess /ges/
hamburger /'hæmbɜːgə(r)/
listen (to) /'lɪsn (tə)/
mime /maɪm/
outside /aʊt'saɪd/
pigeon /'pɪdʒɪn/
programme /'prəʊgræm/
run /rʌn/
take (it in) turns /ˌteɪk (ɪt ˌɪn) 'tɜːnz/
trip /trɪp/
wait (for) /'weɪt (fə)/
young /jʌŋ/

Farm animals
cat /kæt/
calf /kɑːf/
cow /kaʊ/
dog /dɒg/
duck /dʌk/
duckling /'dʌklɪŋ/
foal /fəʊl/
goat /gəʊt/
horse /hɔːs/
kid /kɪd/
kitten /'kɪtn/
lamb /læm/
pig /pɪg/
piglet /'pɪglət/
puppy /'pʌpi/
sheep /ʃiːp/

2B Mickey's model dinosaur
act /ækt/
bone /bəʊn/
dinosaur /'daɪnəsɔː(r)/
ending /'endɪŋ/
glue /gluː/
I'm stuck! /ˌaɪm 'stʌk/
instruction /ɪn'strʌkʃn/
in the afternoon /ˌɪn ði ɑːftə'nuːn/
look for /'lʊk ˌfɔː(r), fə(r)/
magazine /ˌmægə'ziːn/
model /'mɒdl/
mouth /maʊθ/
move /muːv/
rain (r) /reɪn/
something /'sʌmθɪŋ/
Sorry. / I'm sorry. /'sɒri, ˌaɪm 'sɒri/
What's wrong? /ˌwɒts 'rɒŋ/

2C My favourite animals
bark /bɑːk/
description /dɪ'skrɪpʃn/
different /'dɪfrənt/
egg /eg/
elephant /'elɪfənt/
even /'iːvn/
fox /fɒks/
ground /graʊnd/
group /gruːp/

guard /gɑːd/
hole /həʊl/
in the morning /ˌɪn ðə ˈmɔːnɪŋ/
lizard /ˈlɪzəd/
love /lʌv/
meerkat /ˈmɪəkæt/
mouse (mice) /maʊs (maɪs)/
pair /peə(r)/
plant /plɑːnt/
poisonous /ˈpɔɪzənəs/
quite /kwaɪt/
scorpion /ˈskɔːpiən/
size /saɪz/
southern /ˈsʌðən/
stripe /straɪp/
water /ˈwɔːtə(r)/
wildlife park /ˈwaɪldlaɪf ˌpɑːk/
work /wɜːk/

Wild animals
bat /bæt/
camel /ˈkæml/
crocodile /ˈkrɒkədaɪl/
dolphin /ˈdɒlfɪn/
eagle /ˈiːgl/
frog /frɒg/
giraffe /dʒəˈrɑːf/
hippopotamus /hɪpəˈpɒtəməs/
insect /ˈɪnsekt/
kangaroo /ˌkæŋgəˈruː/
monkey /ˈmʌŋki/
shark /ʃɑːk/
tiger /ˈtaɪgə(r)/
zebra /ˈzebrə/

2D The story of Chicken Licken
come with /ˈkʌm ˌwɪð/
den /den/
down /daʊn/
fall (down) /ˌfɔːl (ˈdaʊn)/
farmyard /ˈfɑːmjɑːd/
Follow me. /ˌfɒləʊ ˈmiː/
king /kɪŋ/
meet /miːt/
must /mʌst, məst/
nut /nʌt/
Oh dear! /ˌəʊ ˈdɪə(r)/
pond /pɒnd/
put out the rubbish /ˌpʊt ˌaʊt ðə ˈrʌbɪʃ/
road /rəʊd/
side /saɪd/
sky /skaɪ/
stop /stɒp/
suddenly /ˈsʌdənli/
tell /tel/
village /ˈvɪlɪdʒ/
wash up /ˌwɒʃ ˈʌp/
way /weɪ/
while /waɪl/
wife (wives) /waɪf (waɪvz)/

Culture
apart from /əˈpɑːt frəm/
bear /beə(r)/
bird-watching /ˈbɜːd ˌwɒtʃɪŋ/
build /bɪld/
building /ˈbɪldɪŋ/
butterfly /ˈbʌtəflaɪ/
come out /ˌkʌm ˈaʊt/
common /ˈkɒmən/
countryside /ˈkʌntrisaɪd/
deer /dɪə(r)/
disappear /dɪsəˈpɪə(r)/
escape /ɪˈskeɪp/
food /fuːd/
gardener /ˈgɑːdnə(r)/
government /ˈgʌvənmənt/
hedgehog /ˈhedʒhɒg/
hobby /ˈhɒbi/
in danger /ˌɪn ˈdeɪndʒə(r)/
knock down /ˌnɒk ˈdaʊn/
large /lɑːdʒ/
local /ˈləʊkl/
mention /ˈmenʃn/
most /məʊst/

of course /əv ˈkɔːs/
owl /aʊl/
panther /ˈpænθə(r)/
paragraph /ˈpærəgrɑːf/
pest /pest/
protect /prəˈtekt/
pupil /ˈpjuːpl/
rare /reə(r)/
restaurant /ˈrestrɒnt/
safari park /səˈfɑːri ˌpɑːk/
south-west /ˌsaʊθ ˈwest/
squirrel /ˈskwɪrəl/
topic /ˈtɒpɪk/
town /taʊn/
try /traɪ/
wallaby /ˈwɒləbi/
wild /waɪld/
wolf (wolves) /wʊlf (wʊlvz)/
zoo /zuː/

English Across The Curriculum
air /eə(r)/
amphibian /æmˈfɪbiən/
backbone /ˈbækbəʊn/
breathe /briːð/
carp /kɑːp/
classification /ˌklæsɪfɪˈkeɪʃn/
cold-blooded /ˌkəʊld ˈblʌdɪd/
control /kənˈtrəʊl/
fast /fɑːst/
fly /flaɪ/
fresh /freʃ/
instead /ɪnˈsted/
keep /kiːp/
land (n) /lænd/
lay eggs /ˌleɪ ˈegz/
mammal /ˈmæml/
milk /mɪlk/
more /mɔː(r)/
produce (v) /prəˈdjuːs/
reptile /ˈreptaɪl/
swimmer /ˈswɪmə(r)/
temperature /ˈtemprətʃə(r)/
turtle /ˈtɜːtl/
type /taɪp/
unusual /ʌnˈjuːʒuəl/
vertebrate /ˈvɜːtɪbrət/
warm-blooded /ˌwɔːm ˈblʌdɪd/
whale /weɪl/

Revision
grass /grɑːs/
on the phone /ˌɒn ðə ˈfəʊn/
wake up /ˌweɪk ˈʌp/
zoo keeper /ˈzuː ˌkiːpə(r)/

Your Project
alone /əˈləʊn/
cave /keɪv/
from side to side /frəm ˌsaɪd tə ˈsaɪd/
funny /ˈfʌni/
get on /ˌget ˈɒn/
high /haɪ/
interesting /ˈɪntrəstɪŋ/
look like /ˈlʊk ˌlaɪk/
nearly /ˈnɪəli/
organize /ˈɔːgənaɪz/
reach /riːtʃ/
sway /sweɪ/

3 Holidays

3A Where were you last weekend?
apartment /əˈpɑːtmənt/
away /əˈweɪ/
beach /biːtʃ/
expression /ɪkˈspreʃn/
far /fɑː(r)/
hope /həʊp/
ill /ɪl/
off /ɒf/
Really? /ˈriːəli, ˈrɪəli/
sir /sɜː(r)/

sports instructor /ˈspɔːts ɪnˌstrʌktə(r)/
theme park /ˈθiːm ˌpɑːk/
wedding /ˈwedɪŋ/
weekend /wiːkˈend/

Phrases with at, in, on
at a theme park /ət ə ˈθiːm ˌpɑːk/
at a wedding /ət ə ˈwedɪŋ/
at home /ət ˈhəʊm/
at school /ət ˈskuːl/
at work /ət ˈwɜːk/
in bed /ˌɪn ˈbed/
in the garden /ˌɪn ðə ˈgɑːdn/
in the park /ˌɪn ðə ˈpɑːk/
on holiday /ˌɒn ˈhɒlədeɪ/
on the beach /ˌɒn ðə ˈbiːtʃ/

3B Our holiday
angry /ˈæŋgri/
ask /ɑːsk/
car wash /ˈkɑː ˌwɒʃ/
close (v) /kləʊz/
collect /kəˈlekt/
enjoy /ɪnˈdʒɔɪ/
grab /græb/
land (v) /lænd/
notice /ˈnəʊtɪs/
pack /pæk/
phone call /ˈfəʊn ˌkɔːl/
pick up /ˌpɪk ˈʌp/
pocket /ˈpɒkɪt/
shopping list /ˈʃɒpɪŋ ˌlɪst/
shout /ʃaʊt/
someone else /ˌsʌmwʌn ˈels/
thanks (for) /ˈθæŋks fə(r)/
travel /ˈtrævl/
unpack /ʌnˈpæk/
want /wɒnt/

Holidays
airport /ˈeəpɔːt/
campsite /ˈkæmpsaɪt/
caravan /ˈkærəvæn/
label /ˈleɪbl/
luggage /ˈlʌgɪdʒ/
passenger /ˈpæsɪndʒə(r)/
passport /ˈpɑːspɔːt/
plane /pleɪn/
rucksack /ˈrʌksæk/
runway /ˈrʌnweɪ/
suitcase /ˈsuːtkeɪs/
taxi /ˈtæksi/
tent /tent/
ticket /ˈtɪkɪt/
trolley /ˈtrɒli/

3C Holiday problems
by boat /ˌbaɪ ˈbəʊt/
drive /draɪv/
drop /drɒp/
Greetings from ... /ˈgriːtɪŋz frəm/
have an accident /ˌhæv ən ˈæksɪdənt/
hurt /hɜːt/
irregular /ɪˈregjələ/
journey /ˈdʒɜːni/
luckily /ˈlʌkɪli/
not ... any more /ˌnɒt ... ˌeni ˈmɔː(r)/
on the way /ˌɒn ðə ˈweɪ/
out of /ˈaʊt əv/
painful /ˈpeɪnfl/
piece of paper /ˌpiːs əv ˈpeɪpə(r)/
postcard /ˈpəʊstkɑːd/
regular /ˈregjələ(r)/
separate (adj) /ˈseprət/
spooky /ˈspuːki/
top /tɒp/
waiter /ˈweɪtə(r)/

Holiday problems
bite /baɪt/
break /breɪk/
fall over /ˌfɔːl ˈəʊvə(r)/
feel seasick /ˌfiːl ˈsiːsɪk/
forget /fəˈget/
get lost /ˌget ˈlɒst/
leave /liːv/

lose /luːz/
miss /mɪs/
steal /stiːl/
take the wrong bus /ˌteɪk ðə ˌrɒŋ 'bʌs/

3D Mut's holiday
go camping /ˌgəʊ 'kæmpɪŋ/
go sailing /ˌgəʊ 'seɪlɪŋ/
look after /ˌlʊk 'ɑːftə(r)/
picnic /'pɪknɪk/
unhappy /ʌn'hæpi/

Culture
abroad /ə'brɔːd/
by car /ˌbaɪ 'kɑː(r)/
cathedral /kə'θiːdrəl/
end /end/
environment /ɪn'vaɪrənmənt/
exciting /ɪk'saɪtɪŋ/
famous /'feɪməs/
ferry /'feri/
go away /ˌgəʊ ə'weɪ/
sights /saɪts/
spend /spend/
tourist /'tʊərɪst/
tunnel /'tʌnl/
university /ˌjuːnɪ'vɜːsəti/
visitor /'vɪzɪtə(r)/

English Across the Curriculum
a few /ə 'fjuː/
ago /ə'gəʊ/
at first /ət 'fɜːst/
century /'sentʃəri/
change /tʃeɪndʒ/
cheap /tʃiːp/
dangerous /'deɪndʒərəs/
everywhere /'evriweə(r)/
expensive /ɪk'spensɪv/
factory /'fæktri/
for short /fə 'ʃɔːt/
front /frʌnt/
history /'hɪstri/
however /haʊ'evə(r)/
invent /ɪn'vent/
later /'leɪtə(r)/
motorcycle /'məʊtəsaɪkl/
motor vehicle /'məʊtə ˌviːəkl/
ordinary /'ɔːdnri/
over /'əʊvə(r)/
past /pɑːst/
pedal /'pedl/
push /pʊʃ/
railway /'reɪlweɪ/
rich /rɪtʃ/
soon /suːn/
thousand /'θaʊznd/
transport /'trænspɔːt/
wheel /wiːl/
wooden /'wʊdn/

Revision
finally /'faɪnəli/
make friends /ˌmeɪk 'frendz/
rush /rʌʃ/
terrible /'terəbl/

Your Project
choose /tʃuːz/
copy /'kɒpi/
draft /drɑːft/
fun /fʌn/
memory stick /'meməri ˌstɪk/
mistake /mɪ'steɪk/
seem /siːm/
since /sɪns/
take away /ˌteɪk ə'weɪ/

4 Food

4A Food and drink
Anything else? /ˌeniθɪŋ 'els/
Here you are. /'hɪə juː ˌɑː(r)/
kind /kaɪnd/
lunchbox /'lʌntʃbɒks/

menu /'menjuː/
mixed /mɪkst/
order /'ɔːdə(r)/

Food and drink
banana /bə'nɑːnə/
beans /biːnz/
beef /biːf/
cheese /tʃiːz/
cheeseburger /'tʃiːzbɜːgə(r)/
chicken /'tʃɪkɪn/
chips /tʃɪps/
coffee /'kɒfi/
cola /'kəʊlə/
cream /kriːm/
dessert /dɪ'zɜːt/
drink /drɪŋk/
egg /eg/
fish /fɪʃ/
fruit /fruːt/
grapes /greɪps/
hot chocolate /ˌhɒt 'tʃɒklət/
ice-cream /ˌaɪs 'kriːm/
lamb /læm/
lemonade /ˌlemə'neɪd/
lettuce /'letɪs/
meat /miːt/
milkshake /'mɪlkʃeɪk/
orange juice /'ɒrɪndʒ ˌdʒuːs/
pasta /'pæstə/
pie /paɪ/
pork /pɔːk/
rice /raɪs/
salad /'sæləd/
salmon /'sæmən/
satsuma /sæt'suːmə/
spaghetti bolognese /spəˌgeti bɒlə'naɪz/
tea /tiː/
tomato /tə'mɑːtəʊ/
tuna /'tjuːnə/
vegetable /'vedʒtəbl/

4B Stone soup
almost /'ɔːlməʊst/
another /ə'nʌðə(r)/
any /'eni/
anyone /'eniwʌn/
bottle /'bɒtl/
bread /bred/
bring back /ˌbrɪŋ 'bæk/
butter /'bʌtə(r)/
cabbage /'kæbɪdʒ/
carrot /'kærət/
come back /ˌkʌm 'bæk/
crisps /krɪsps/
cut up /ˌkʌt 'ʌp/
delicious /dɪ'lɪʃəs/
diet /'daɪət/
Excuse me. /ɪk'skjuːz ˌmiː/
fetch /fetʃ/
find out /ˌfaɪnd 'aʊt/
ham /hæm/
healthy /'helθi/
knock /nɒk/
lemon /'lemən/
loaf /ləʊf/
magic /'mædʒɪk/
milk /mɪlk/
mushroom /'mʌʃrʊm, -uːm/
normal /'nɔːml/
onion /'ʌnjən/
pepper /'pepə(r)/
pity /'pɪti/
potato /pə'teɪtəʊ/
ready /'redi/
salt /sɔːlt, sɒlt/
saucepan /'sɔːspən/
sausage /'sɒsɪdʒ/
slice /slaɪs/
soup /suːp/
spoon /spuːn/
stone /stəʊn/
sugar /'ʃʊgə(r)/
taste /teɪst/
tramp /træmp/
water /'wɔːtə(r)/

whether /'weðə(r)/
wine /waɪn/
yoghurt /'jɒgət/

4C Mut goes shopping
apple juice /'æpl ˌdʒuːs/
At last! /ət 'lɑːst/
bar /bɑː(r)/
bunch /bʌntʃ/
carton /'kɑːtn/
gram /græm/
How much ...? /'haʊ ˌmʌtʃ/
packet /'pækɪt/
pot /pɒt/
quantity /'kwɒntəti/
shelf /ʃelf/
tin /tɪn/
worried /'wʌrid/

4D Emma's apple crumble
apple crumble /ˌæpl 'krʌmbl/
boil /bɔɪl/
bowl /bəʊl/
cover /'kʌvə(r)/
degree /dɪ'griː/
dish /dɪʃ/
flour /'flaʊə(r)/
fry /fraɪ/
frying pan /'fraɪɪŋ ˌpæn/
grate /greɪt/
grill /grɪl/
half a / an /'hɑːf ə, ən/
ingredient /ɪn'griːdiənt/
margarine /ˌmɑːdʒə'riːn/
melt /melt/
mix /mɪks/
mixture /'mɪkstʃə(r)/
oven /ʌvn/
peas /piːz/
peel /piːl/
peeler /'piːlə(r)/
pour /pɔː(r)/
recipe /'resəpi/
sauce /sɔːs/
serve /sɜːv/
the rest /ðə 'rest/
toast /təʊst/
vinegar /'vɪnɪgə(r)/
Welsh rarebit /ˌwelʃ 'reəbɪt/

Culture
bacon /'beɪkən/
baked beans /ˌbeɪkt 'biːnz/
canteen /kæn'tiːn/
cereal /'sɪəriəl/
curry /'kʌri/
custard /'kʌstəd/
grapefruit /'greɪpfruːt/
honey /'hʌni/
jam /dʒæm/
lasagne /lə'zænjə, -'sænjə/
light /laɪt/
main course /ˌmeɪn 'kɔːs/
marmalade /'mɑːməleɪd/
midday /mɪd'deɪ/
nowadays /'naʊədeɪz/
pudding /'pʊdɪŋ/
risotto /rɪ'zɒtəʊ/
such as /'sʌtʃ əz/
supper /'sʌpə(r)/
vegetarian /ˌvedʒə'teəriən/

English Across the Curriculum
around /ə'raʊnd/
avocado /ˌævə'kɑːdəʊ/
Aztecs /'æzteks/
bring /brɪŋ/
cool /kuːl/
grow /grəʊ/
language /'læŋgwɪdʒ/
maize /meɪz/
seed /siːd/
spread /spred/
sweetcorn /'swiːtkɔːn/
wet /wet/

Revision

circle /'sɜːkl/
cut out /ˌkʌt 'aʊt/
parcel /'pɑːsl/
plastic /'plæstɪk/
puzzle /'pʌzl/
round /raʊnd/
stir /stɜː(r)/

Your Project

celebrity chef /səˌlebrəti 'ʃef/
replace /rɪ'pleɪs/
sticky /'stɪki/
take a photo /ˌteɪk ə 'fəʊtəʊ/
toffee /'tɒfi/

5 The world

5A My country

beautiful /'bjuːtɪfl/
capital /'kæpɪtl/
coast /kəʊst/
deep /diːp/
map /mæp/
million /'mɪljən/
monster /'mɒnstə(r)/
wide /waɪd/
wood /wʊd/

Places

beach /biːtʃ/
bridge /brɪdʒ/
canal /kə'næl/
cliff /klɪf/
field /fiːld/
forest /'fɒrɪst/
harbour /'hɑːbə(r)/
hill /hɪl/
island /'aɪlənd/
lake /leɪk/
motorway /'məʊtəweɪ/
mountain /'maʊntən/
power station /'paʊə ˌsteɪʃn/
river /'rɪvə(r)/
sea /siː/
skyscraper /'skaɪskreɪpə(r)/
tunnel /'tʌnl/
valley /'væli/

5B North and south

crowded /'kraʊdɪd/
difference /'dɪfrəns/
difficult /'dɪfɪkəlt/
east /iːst/
except /ɪk'sept/
flat (adj) /flæt/
friendly /'frendli/
hilly /'hɪli/
low /ləʊ/
north /nɔːθ/
north-west /ˌnɔːθ 'west/
rule /ruːl/
season /'siːzn/
south /saʊθ/
south-east /ˌsaʊθ 'iːst/
west /west/
yesterday /'jestədeɪ/

The weather

It's cloudy. /ˌɪts 'klaʊdi/
It's cold. /ˌɪts 'kəʊld/
It's cool. /ˌɪts 'kuːl/
It's dry. /ˌɪts 'draɪ/
It's fine. /ˌɪts 'faɪn/
It's foggy. /ˌɪts 'fɒgi/
It's freezing. /ˌɪts 'friːzɪŋ/
It's hot. /ˌɪts 'hɒt/
It's icy. /ˌɪts 'aɪsi/
It's raining. /ˌɪts 'reɪnɪŋ/
It's snowing. /ˌɪts 'snəʊɪŋ/
It's sunny. /ˌɪts 'sʌni/
It's warm. /ˌɪts 'wɔːm/
It's wet. /ˌɪts 'wet/
It's windy. /ˌɪts 'wɪndi/

5C Record breakers

cheetah /'tʃiːtə/
clue /kluː/
continent /'kɒntɪnənt/
gold /gəʊld/
iron /'aɪən/
lead (n) /led/
lion /'laɪən/
metal /'metl/
ostrich /'ɒstrɪtʃ/
record (n) /'rekɔːd/
sportsperson /'spɔːtspɜːsn/

5D Mickey and Millie go camping

area /'eəriə/
as … as … /əz … əz/
better /'betə(r)/
Beware of … /bɪ'weər əv/
bull /bʊl/
describe /dɪ'skraɪb/
feather /'feðə/
football team /'fʊtbɔːl ˌtiːm/
full (of) /'fʊl (əv)/
get dark /ˌget 'dɑːk/
guide /gaɪd/
guidebook /'gaɪdbʊk/
ice /aɪs/
lightning /'laɪtnɪŋ/
pop group /'pɒp ˌgruːp/
runner /'rʌnə(r)/
sign /saɪn/
snore /snɔː(r)/
translate /træns'leɪt/
view /vjuː/
worse /wɜːs/
worst /wɜːst/

Culture

across /ə'krɒs/
barbecue /'bɑːbɪkjuː/
blackberry /'blækbəri/
bluebell /'bluːbel/
chilly /'tʃɪli/
climate /'klaɪmət/
cloud /klaʊd/
come in /ˌkʌm 'ɪn/
daffodil /'dæfədɪl/
eastern /'iːstən/
fête /feɪt/
frosty /'frɒsti/
hay fever /'heɪ ˌfiːvə(r)/
hurricane /'hʌrɪkən/
saying /'seɪɪŋ/
shower /'ʃaʊə/
sports day /'spɔːts ˌdeɪ/
storm /stɔːm/

English Across the Curriculum

federal /'fedərəl/
flag /flæg/
form /fɔːm/
Hawaii /hə'waɪi/
original /ə'rɪdʒənl/
population /pɒpju'leɪʃn/
president /'prezɪdənt/
settler /'setlə(r)/
star (n) /stɑː(r)/
state /steɪt/
time zone /'taɪm ˌzəʊn/
whole /həʊl/

Revision

boring /'bɔːrɪŋ/
flight /flaɪt/

Your Project

as long as /əz 'lɒŋ əz/
copy /'kɒpi/
download (v) /daʊn'ləʊd/
fact /fækt/
information /ɪnfə'meɪʃn/
invitation /ɪnvɪ'teɪʃn/
It doesn't matter. /ɪt 'dʌznt ˌmætə(r)/
laughing /'lɑːfɪŋ/
nation /'neɪʃn/

present (v) /prɪ'zent/
search engine /'sɜːtʃ ˌendʒɪn/
singing /'sɪŋɪŋ/
tourism /'tʊərɪzəm/
website /'websaɪt/
word /wɜːd/

6 Entertainment

6A TV programmes

hall /hɔːl/
perfect /'pɜːfɪkt/
record (v) /rɪ'kɔːd/
remote control /rɪˌməʊt kən'trəʊl/
revise /rɪ'vaɪz/
test /test/
TV set /ˌtiː 'viː ˌset/

Types of TV programmes

cartoon /kɑː'tuːn/
chat show /'tʃæt ˌʃəʊ/
comedy programme /'kɒmədi ˌprəʊgræm/
documentary /dɒkju'mentri/
film /fɪlm/
nature programme /'neɪtʃə ˌprəʊgræm/
police drama /pə'liːs ˌdrɑːmə/
quiz show /'kwɪz ˌʃəʊ/
reality show /ri'æləti ˌʃəʊ/
soap opera /'səʊp ˌɒprə/
sports programme /'spɔːts ˌprəʊgræm/
the news /ðə 'njuːz/

6B At the movies

Are you all right? /ˌɑː ˌjuː ˌɔːl 'raɪt/
belt /belt/
blanket /'blæŋkɪt/
bottom /'bɒtəm/
briefcase /'briːfkeɪs/
by /baɪ/
carefully /'keəfəli/
computer chip /kəm'pjuːtə ˌtʃɪp/
die /daɪ/
easily /'iːzəli/
enemy /'enəmi/
engine /'endʒɪn/
happily /'hæpɪli/
hard /hɑːd/
horrible /'hɒrəbl/
horribly /'hɒrəbli/
imagine /ɪ'mædʒɪn/
laugh /lɑːf/
lock /lɒk/
loud /laʊd/
loudly /'laʊdli/
movie /'muːvi/
pull /pʊl/
quick /kwɪk/
quickly /'kwɪkli/
quiet /'kwaɪət/
quietly /'kwaɪətli/
reporter /rɪ'pɔːtə(r)/
sad /sæd/
sadly /'sædli/
safe /seɪf/
safely /'seɪfli/
satellite /'sætəlaɪt/
save /seɪv/
seat /siːt/
secret /'siːkrət/
sink /sɪŋk/
slow /sləʊ/
slowly /'sləʊli/
stomach /'stʌmək/
sudden /'sʌdn/
well /wel/
whisper /'wɪspə(r)/

6C Lights, cameras, action

Action! /'ækʃn/
actress /'æktrəs/
correctly /kə'rektli/
dentist /'dentɪst/
line /laɪn/
scene /siːn/

Types of films
adventure film /əd'ventʃə ˌfɪlm/
cartoon /kɑː'tuːn/
comedy film /'kɒmədi ˌfɪlm/
fantasy /'fæntəsi/
horror film /'hɒrə ˌfɪlm/
musical /'mjuːzɪkl/
romcom (romantic comedy) /'rɒmkɒm
  (rəʊˌmæntɪk 'kɒmədi)/
sci-fi film (science fiction) /'saɪ ˌfaɪ ˌfɪlm
  (ˌsaɪəns 'fɪkʃn)/
thriller /'θrɪlə(r)/
western /'westən/

6D The lost penguin
bus stop /'bʌs ˌstɒp/
Let's ... /lets/
policeman /pə'liːsmən/
Shall we ...? /ˌʃæl, ʃəl wiː '.../
suggest /sə'dʒest/
suggestion /sə'dʒestʃn/
What shall we do? /ˌwɒt ʃəl wi 'duː/
Where shall we meet? /ˌweə ʃəl wi 'miːt/
Why don't you ...? /'waɪ ˌdəʊnt ˌjuː/

Culture
actor /'æktə(r)/
adventure /əd'ventʃə(r)/
appear /ə'pɪə(r)/
assistant /ə'sɪstənt/
character /'kærəktə(r)/
create /kri'eɪt/
creator /kri'eɪtə(r)/
detective /dɪ'tektɪv/
evil /'iːvl/
fight /faɪt/
film star /'fɪlm ˌstɑː(r)/
hero /'hɪərəʊ/
international /ˌɪntə'næʃnəl/
inventor /ɪn'ventə(r)/
modern /'mɒdn/
plasticine /'plæstəsiːn/
secret agent /ˌsiːkrət 'eɪdʒənt/
star (v) /stɑː(r)/
TV series /ˌtiː 'viː ˌsɪəriːz/
win /wɪn/
wizard /'wɪzəd/

English Across the Curriculum
bored /bɔːd/
camcorder /'kæmkɔːdə(r)/
cameraperson /'kæmrəpɜːsn/
director /də'rektə(r), dɪ-, daɪ-/
edit /'edɪt/
equipment /ɪ'kwɪpmənt/
especially /ɪ'speʃəli/
excellent /'eksələnt/
feel sick /ˌfiːl 'sɪk/
hold /həʊld/
indoors /ɪn'dɔːz/
just /dʒʌst/
lighting /'laɪtɪŋ/
media studies /'miːdiə ˌstʌdiz/
microphone /'maɪkrəfəʊn/
premiere /'premieə(r)/
script /skrɪpt/
soundperson /'saʊndpɜːsn/
tip /tɪp/
tripod /'traɪpɒd/
useful /'juːsfl/
voice /vɔɪs/

Your Project
channel /'tʃænl/
entertainment /ˌentə'teɪnmənt/
nothing /'nʌθɪŋ/
opinion /ə'pɪnjən/
pretty /'prɪti/
review /rɪ'vjuː/
screen /skriːn/
settle /'setl/
survey (n) /'sɜːveɪ/
turn down /ˌtɜːn 'daʊn/

Reading
Unit 1
attic /'ætɪk/
axe /æks/
branch /brɑːntʃ/
cart /kɑːt/
chop (down) /ˌtʃɒp ('daʊn)/
corner /'kɔːnə(r)/
fire /'faɪə(r)/
fir tree /'fɜː ˌtriː/
hang /hæŋ/
inside /ɪn'saɪd/
living room /'lɪvɪŋ ˌruːm/
piece /piːs/
point /pɔɪnt/
proud /praʊd/
sail /seɪl/
servant /'sɜːvənt/
ship /ʃɪp/
silver /'sɪlvə(r)/
ugly /'ʌgli/

Unit 2
councillor /'kaʊnsələ(r)/
drown /draʊn/
ever /'evə(r)/
flute /fluːt/
get rid of /ˌget 'rɪd əv/
Mayor /meə(r)/
offer /'ɒfə(r)/
pay /peɪ/
please /pliːz/
through /θruː/
too much /'tuː ˌmʌtʃ/
town hall /ˌtaʊn 'hɔːl/

Unit 3
dirty /'dɜːti/
entrance /'entrəns/
genie /'dʒiːni/
golden /'gəʊldən/
in a flash /ˌɪn ə 'flæʃ/
jewel /'dʒuːəl/
lamp /læmp/
lift /lɪft/
live happily ever after /ˌlɪv ˌhæpɪli ˌevər
  'ɑːftə(r)/
long ago /ˌlɒŋ ə'gəʊ/
magician /mə'dʒɪʃn/
marry /'mæri/
master /'mɑːstə(r)/
moment /'məʊmənt/
out /aʊt/
palace /'pæləs/
pedlar /'pedlə(r)/
poor /pɔː(r)/
prince /prɪns/
princess /prɪn'ses/
prison /'prɪzn/
ring (n) /rɪŋ/
rock /rɒk/
rub /rʌb/
wicked /'wɪkɪd/

Unit 4
African /'æfrɪkən/
bake /beɪk/
go to sleep /ˌgəʊ tə 'sliːp/
have a rest /ˌhæv ə 'rest/
lie down /ˌlaɪ 'daʊn/
look down /ˌlʊk 'daʊn/
noisy /'nɔɪzi/
Once upon a time ... /'wʌns əˌpɒn ə ˌtaɪm/
See you later. /'siː ˌjuː ˌleɪtə(r)/
share /ʃeə(r)/
spin /spɪn/
smell /smel/
Thank you. /'θæŋk ˌjuː/
walk on /'wɔːk ˌɒn/
web /web/

Unit 5
climb /klaɪm/
farmer /'fɑːmə(r)/
legend /'ledʒənd/
pick flowers /ˌpɪk 'flaʊəz/
polite /pə'laɪt/
run away /ˌrʌn ə'weɪ/
scream /skriːm/
stand up /ˌstænd 'ʌp/
stepdaughter /'stepdɔːtə(r)/
strawberry /'strɔːbəri/
widow /'wɪdəʊ/

Unit 6
angrily /'æŋgrəli/
cry /kraɪ/
cut off /ˌkʌt 'ɒf/
dead /ded/
god /gɒd/
goddess /'gɒdes/
helmet /'helmɪt/
instantly /'ɪnstəntli/
invisible /ɪn'vɪzəbl/
invite /ɪn'vaɪt/
just in time /ˌdʒʌst ˌɪn 'taɪm/
kiss /kɪs/
mirror /'mɪrə(r)/
put on /ˌpʊt 'ɒn/
shield /ʃiːld/
statue /'stætʃuː/
sword /sɔːd/
take off /ˌteɪk 'ɒf/
temple /'templ/

Irregular verbs
Infinitive / Past simple

Infinitive / Past simple	Infinitive / Past simple
can / could	lose / lost
be / was, were	make / made
become / became	mean / meant
begin / began	pay / paid
bite / bit	put / put
break / broke	read / read
bring / brought	ride / rode
build / built	ring / rang
burn / burnt	run / ran
buy / bought	say / said
catch / caught	see / saw
come / came	sell / sold
cost / cost	send / sent
cut / cut	set / set
do / did	sing / sang
draw / drew	sink / sank
drink / drank	sit / sat
drive / drove	smell / smelt
eat / ate	speak / spoke
fall / fell	spell / spelt
feel / felt	spend / spent
fight / fought	stand / stood
find / found	steal / stole
fly / flew	stick / stuck
get / got	sweep / swept
give / gave	swim / swam
go / went	take / took
grow / grew	teach / taught
have / had	tear / tore
hear / heard	tell / told
hide / hid	think / thought
hit / hit	throw / threw
hold / held	understand / understood
hurt / hurt	wake / woke
keep / kept	wear / wore
know / knew	win / won
learn / learnt	write / wrote
leave / left	

PHONETIC SYMBOLS

iː	as in	see /siː/	t	as in	tea /tiː/
ɪ	as in	sit /sɪt/	d	as in	did /dɪd/
e	as in	ten /ten/	k	as in	cat /kæt/
æ	as in	hat /hæt/	g	as in	got /gɒt/
ɑː	as in	arm /ɑːm/	tʃ	as in	chin /tʃɪn/
ɒ	as in	got /gɒt/	dʒ	as in	June /dʒuːn/
ɔː	as in	saw /sɔː/	f	as in	fall /fɔːl/
ʊ	as in	put /pʊt/	v	as in	voice /vɔɪs/
uː	as in	too /tuː/	θ	as in	thin /θɪn/
ʌ	as in	cup /kʌp/	ð	as in	then /ðen/
ɜː	as in	fur /fɜː(r)/	s	as in	so /səʊ/
ə	as in	ago /əˈgəʊ/	z	as in	zoo /zuː/
eɪ	as in	page /peɪdʒ/	ʃ	as in	she /ʃiː/
əʊ	as in	home /həʊm/	ʒ	as in	vision /ˈvɪʒn/
aɪ	as in	five /faɪv/	h	as in	how /haʊ/
aʊ	as in	now /naʊ/	m	as in	man /mæn/
ɔɪ	as in	join /dʒɔɪn/	n	as in	no /nəʊ/
ɪə	as in	near /nɪə(r)/	ŋ	as in	sing /sɪŋ/
eə	as in	hair /heə(r)/	l	as in	leg /leg/
ʊə	as in	pure /pjʊə(r)/	r	as in	red /red/
p	as in	pen /pen/	j	as in	yes /jes/
b	as in	bad /bæd/	w	as in	wet /wet/

OXFORD
UNIVERSITY PRESS

Great Clarendon Street, Oxford, OX2 6DP, United Kingdom

Oxford University Press is a department of the University of Oxford.
It furthers the University's objective of excellence in research, scholarship,
and education by publishing worldwide. Oxford is a registered trade
mark of Oxford University Press in the UK and in certain other countries

© Oxford University Press 2013

The moral rights of the author have been asserted

First published in 2013

2018

10 9 8

No unauthorized photocopying

ISBN: 9780 19 476511 4   Workbook
ISBN: 9780 19 476553 4   Audio CD
ISBN: 9780 19 476736 1   Access Card
ISBN: 9780 19 476738 5   Online Practice
ISBN: 9780 19 476290 8   Pack

Printed in China

This book is printed on paper from certified and well-managed sources

ACKNOWLEDGEMENTS

*The author and publisher are very grateful to all the teachers who have offered their
comments and suggestions which have been invaluable in the development of Project
Fourth edition. We would particularly like to mention those who helped by writing
reports on Project:*

Slovenia: Jezerka Beškovnik, Andreja Hazabent Habe, Jelena Novak

Croatia: Ela Ivanić

Czech Republic: Jana Pecháčková, Petra Gušlová, Jana Ferancová, Šárka
Karpíšková

Slovakia: Mgr. Bronislava Gulánová, Mgr. Peter Humay, Mgr. Katarina Tóth
Mikócziová, Mgr.Monika Szilvaová, Mgr. Annamaria Zátik

Hungary: Szilvia Csanády, Csilla Papné Szalay, Melinda Bollog, Zsuzsanna
Győrfi, Katalin Füle

Serbia: Sonja Preda Foljan, Ljiljana Ćuzović, Ana Jovanić, Emina Milošević,
Nataša Milosavljević

Cover artwork by: Paul Daviz

The publisher would like to thank the following for permission to reproduce photographs:
Corbis pp.8 (boy with cap/Ocean), 8 (girl playing tennis/Ben Welsh/Design
Pics); Getty Images p.30 (The Statue of Liberty/Mai/Mai/Time & Life Pictures);
Oxford University Press pp.45 (London Eye/Image Source), 45 (Eiffel Tower/
Photodisc).

Illustrations by: DTP Gecko p.53 (ex.5); Glyn Goodwin p.19 (ex.5); Phil Healey
p.48; Javier Joaquin/The Organisation pp.6, 11, 15, 25, 27, 31, 42, 56; Chris
Pavely pp.4, 9, 14 (ex.2), 18, 21, 26, 32, 33, 36, 40, 44, 50, 59, 63; Jorge Santillan/
Beehive pp.2, 10, 13, 19 (ex.4), 24, 28, 38, 39, 47, 54, 57, 64; Si Smith pp.3, 5, 7,
12, 14 (ex.3), 16, 17, 20, 22, 23, 29, 34, 35, 37, 43, 46, 51, 52, 53 (I can), 58, 60, 61.